COGNITIVE BEHAVIORAL THERAPY (CBT) **WORKBOOK**

Table of Contents

Introduction to Cognitive Behavioral Therapy

What is CBT? Your User's Manual

You were probably never told that you are the owner of the most powerful machine on the planet—the human mind! It is what allow us humans to paint masterpieces, build modern marvels, make scientific discoveries, and learn through courses like this one. But unfortunately, our minds don't come with an instruction manual.

Most people never reach their potential because their machines—the most powerful tool they will ever have—inherited faulty programming. But it's not their fault—they were never taught how their mind works, how to reprogram it, or how much power they have to create the lives they want.

You were probably never taught that you have the ability to change ANYTHING about yourself—your level of intelligence, your talent, your abilities, and your personality.

You were probably never taught that you have the ability to control your thoughts, emotions, and behaviors, and you certainly weren't taught how.

You may have been told you could be or do anything you wanted when you grew up, but you never believed it (and neither did the people who told you this). You were surrounded by people who settled in life, who were unhappy, who were dysfunctional and who, unfortunately, passed the beliefs and patterns of thinking that got them there onto you.

Now you're grown up and you have a million thoughts that run through your mind that make you doubt yourself and believe your dreams aren't possible.

Like most people, you've got a monkey mind that's always negative and distracting you from creating the life you want.

It's time to give your monkey mind a banana. This course is the banana!

This course will teach you how your mind works, including the #1 most important thing you could ever understand about yourself, which is that your thoughts are what create your emotions.

That's right, even though it seems like the situations or people around you are causing you to feel a certain way, the truth is that it is what you THINK about the situation that causes your emotion.

Knowing this gives you your power back because through this course you can learn how to CHOOSE YOUR THOUGHTS. By doing so you can control your emotions and ultimately create your destiny.

In this course you will learn how to reprogram your mind and avoid the ultimate form of failure, which is to achieve success in your life but still feel unfulfilled.

You'll learn how your thoughts and emotions work and how to identify why you think and act the way you do. You'll develop self-awareness so you can stop negative thinking in the act and retrain your monkey mind to think more positively and rationally.

What is CBT?

The core premise is that we have the ability to control our thoughts, emotions, and behaviors, and because of this we can create the life experiences we want.

CBT stands for cognitive behavioral therapy and in coaching it's also referred to as cognitive behavioral technique.

Cognitive refers to the process of learning and understanding through our experience, what we take in through the 5 senses, and what we think about all of it. Cognitive processes happen both consciously, meaning we are aware of them, and unconsciously, meaning they happen automatically, without our awareness.

Behavior refers to the way we act, which can happen deliberately—when we are aware of our cognitive processes, or reactively—when we are responding unconsciously to a situation.

The Core Principles of CBT

It is our perception of the situation, rather than the situation itself, that determines how we feel about it and how we react to it.

Our perspective of a situation can change if we change the way we look at it, just like putting on a pair of glasses with a different colored lens or looking at an object from a different angle.

When we have a negative interpretation of a situation, it causes a negative emotional reaction.

Finding a positive viewpoint of a situation leads to improved emotional wellbeing.

The actions we take are chosen based on what we think, and especially how we feel about a situation. Therefore, if we change the way we think, it changes our emotional state, which influences our decision making and leads to better decisions.

When we change our negative thought process, improve our mood, and stop sabotaging behaviors, we are better able to meet our goals.

How Does CBT Work?

Because of these underlying principles, CBT is designed to help us manage our perceptions and interpretations, which can be distorted due to cognitive distortions or errors in thinking, as well as limiting beliefs. It teaches us how to become aware of and then teach us how to think more clearly, and positively. CBT helps us overcome negative, destructive thinking. But, it's not just positive thinking, it's logical, clear-minded, healthy thinking.

If you've ever made assumptions, jumped to conclusions, or made a situation worse than it was by worrying about the worst-case scenario, you have experienced a cognitive distortion.

Many of these faulty ways of thinking are obvious once you know they exist, but you don't notice them in daily life because almost all thinking happens automatically or unconsciously.

CBT also helps you tame the tormenting critical voice in your head and take your power back from others who have implanted limiting beliefs into your mind.

Through CBT you will learn how to:

1. Identify the sources of negative, limiting, destructive thinking.
2. Develop awareness of the emotions and beliefs associated with the negativity.
3. Develop the ability to catch negative thoughts in the act, reframe them, and choose an empowered thought.
4. Practice processes and behaviors to develop positive, rational, empowering thought processes and coping mechanism that you can apply to real life events.

The History of CBT

CBT was founded by psychiatrist Aaron Beck in the 1960s when he noticed a strong correlation between his patients' thought patterns and internal dialog and their emotions and actions. Today this seems like common sense to many people, but at the time it was truly revolutionary. CBT was the first shift in the study and practice in psychology that moved toward the underlying belief that the human mind can be trained and enhanced in order to produce happiness, fulfillment, and optimum performance, and away from the focus on mental disorders and dysfunction. CBT, instead, recognizes the dysfunction of the faulty programming and seeks to reprogram it. Unlike other forms of psychotherapy used then, and today, CBT focuses on the "here an now" thoughts and belief and does not go digging back into the past looking for the root of emotional problems.

By the late 1990's, the positive psychology movement was in full swing, and over the years the evidence that supports the validity of CBT has only continued to grow. The self-help and human potential movement are based on this notion of self-empowerment, as well as the field of life coaching.

Today, CBT is used by counselors, therapists, and coaches who want to teach their clients to change their unwanted behaviors by changing their thought patterns. It can also be useful when the thoughts and emotions themselves are what is problematic, such as obsessive thinking, not being able to stop stewing about things that bother you, destructive self-talk, and self-sabotaging behaviors.

Identifying Problem Areas

There are 7 common problem areas where many people's thinking and behavior holds them back from achieving their goals. You can complete this assessment when thinking about a specific goal you are working on but are having difficulty accomplishing, and then identify which areas are getting in your way. Alternatively, you can complete this assessment when thinking in general about what areas you primarily struggle with. The attached assessment will help you identify the problem areas, the thoughts, emotions, and behaviors that illustrate the problem, and point you toward sections and lections within this program that address that specific problem area. It's like a guide to making the most of the material in this course to help you overcome your roadblocks and move forward toward your goals!

The 7 Common Problem Areas Are:

1. Feeling limited due to not being good at something, perceived low level of ability or intelligence
2. Difficulty making a decision
3. Unable to get started or take action
4. Fear or resistance
5. Self-sabotage or procrastination
6. Negative self-talk and/or limiting thinking and beliefs
7. Stress, overwhelm, anxiety, obsessive thinking, or feeling out of control

Of course, there may be other problems you may be experiencing, so feel free to identify them here. There are also many additional situations that are addressed through the material in this program. As you work your way through the material, you will identify key activities that you find the most helpful for your purposes. This course is meant to provide a repository of insights and tools that you pick and choose from and apply them to the goals you set.

As you identify the areas you will be focusing on, celebrate the progress you have already made by taking the initiative to get to this point! There is no more meaningful work than learning how to use your mind to create your life!

Desired Goal: ____

Problem area:	**Thoughts that illustrate the problem:**	**Emotions or behaviors that illustrate the problem:**
Feeling limited due to not being good at something, perceived low level of ability or intelligence		
Difficulty making a decision		

Unable to get started or take action		
Fear or resistance		
Self-sabotage or procrastination		
Negative self-talk and/or limiting thinking and beliefs		
Stress, overwhelm, anxiety, obsessive thinking, or feeling out of control		
Other		

The Growth Mindset

Why the Growth Mindset is the Key to Changing Your Mind

There is one core underlying belief that needs to be developed in order for CBT to be effective: The Growth Mindset which basically means believing that you CAN change your thoughts and behaviors.

If you don't believe you can change, you won't.

Two Key Underlying Psychological Principles:

1) Locus of control: what you believe is and is not within your control. Some people feel like life is simply happening to them, like they're a victim to whatever might happen. They have an external locus of control.

Other people believe they are in control of their lives. Even when something happens to them that appears to come from the outside, they still see how they have power over the outcome. This is an internal locus of control.

How do you develop an internal locus of control and feel empowered about your life?

2) Develop a bias toward action. If you feel like your life is out of your control, you're unlikely to take action because you don't believe it will make a difference. You have a bias toward inaction. So, in order to overcome this, you can begin taking action and seeing what happens. Doing this over time shows yourself that you have more influence over your life than you thought. You develop a bias toward action, meaning you believe you're the type of person who takes action to influence their own life. This, in turn, develops your internal locus of control and makes you feel empowered to direct your own life. It gives you confidence.

But there is one core underlying psychological principle that is even more important to understand: the Growth Mindset.

People who have this mindset are:

- More resilient
- Better at coping with failure
- More likely to challenge themselves
- Those who do not have it are:
- Less resilient
- Poor at coping with failure
- Avoid challenges that could reveal their flaws

QUIZ:

Consider this example and how you would feel if it was you. Imagine that you had a terrible day. You spilled coffee on your shirt on the way to work, you got a parking ticket on your lunch break, and your boss reprimanded you for publishing a document with several major errors. How would you react?

a) ☐ You'd feel bad about yourself for being clumsy, unintelligent and unlucky. You'd accept that this is just how your life goes.

b) ☐ You'd be upset but you'd be thinking about how you should probably use a better travel mug, be more careful when you park, and double check your work.

Then, answer these questions:

If I told you that your intelligence, like an IQ score, is something about you that you can't change, would you:

a) ☐ agree
b) ☐ disagree

If I told you that talents are something you are born with would you:

a) ☐ agree
b) ☐ disagree

So, did you answer mostly a's or b's?

Before you dive into what this all means, the number 1 most important thing you need to know about it is: If you don't already have this mindset, you can LEARN IT.

This core belief system is called the Growth Mindset. And the opposite way of viewing the world is called the Fixed Mindset.

If you answered all b's, you have a growth mindset. If you answered some a's, that's okay, because your answers to those questions will be very different by the time you finish this course!

Growth Mindset

The growth mindset is a belief that your basic qualities, including intelligence and talent, can be cultivated through effort. This means that while people may be innately different, with certain aptitudes and temperaments, all aspects of a person's abilities and personality can be changed, regardless of where your setpoint is.

Fixed Mindset

The fixed mindset, on the other hand, is a belief that these same characteristics are fixed at birth or become locked-in by a certain age. This means that some people are just inherently more talented or intelligent than others and that's just the way it is.

If you feel like at least part of you believes that intelligence and talent are fixed, you are not alone. Most people, especially in the western world, believe this because our culture teaches us that it's true. So, it's not your fault. Emphasis is put on testing us to determine our intelligence, such as taking an IQ test or being graded. No one stops to think that a single test taken on a certain day at a certain age cannot possibly predict how well you would do on the test years later, after learning more, or when you're in a better mood. But we're taught that these tests identify what we've got and that's it. We're stuck with it.

We also live in a culture that is obsessed with "natural talent". There are 2 problems with this.

1. The people who work hard to develop their abilities far out-win the naturals in the long run.
2. If being a natural is so important, it actually discourages the effort it takes for those who have to work at it.

And that's exactly what happens.

People with a fixed mindset believe they'll always have the same level of talent regardless of how much effort they put in. They've either got it or they don't. Because of this the spend a lot of effort trying to prove their abilities and intelligence. They want to look smart. So, if they're not immediately good at something, they stop doing it. This is because they're in a constant quest to prove that they are talented or intelligent. To a fixed mindset person, effort is a bad thing. Having to work hard at something is a signal that you're not a natural talent or that you're not of high intelligent because if you were you wouldn't' have to try. As a result, they don't challenge themselves, they don't like trying new things, and so they never develop their potential. They're trapped reaching only as far as their current abilities can take them.

They're trapped because failure is devastating. It means they are a failure. And because they don't want to have to take on an identity as a failure, they'll often blame others or the outside world. Fixed mindset people find joy in being the best or being judged as talented or smart.

Growth mindset people see the world very differently. They believe that the more effort they put into something, whether it's practicing or learning, the better they will become. If they're not good at something they see it as a sign that they have to work harder. They have little need to prove they are talented or intelligent and instead are on a never-ending quest to continue to grow. How hard someone tries is how they measure the person's value. They enjoy challenges and see them as an opportunity to learn something and expand their boundaries. They may not like failing, but they don't ever believe they are a failure. They see failure as a learning experience. Growth mindset people find joy in progress and learning.

So, what is important to know here is that if you didn't already know that you can change and improve your talents, skills, intelligence, characteristics, and behaviors, now you know! It's also important to keep in mind that no one is either 100% fixed or 100% growth oriented. Everyone is on a spectrum. Plus, you can think fixed in one area, such as believing your intelligence is fixed, while believe you can grow in another area, such as your singing ability.

And remember, this is important because the rest of this program will be helping you change the way you think so that you can change the way you behave, which will change your experience of life in any area that desire. Understanding the growth mindset matters because if you want to develop your confidence you have to believe that your level of confidence is not limited by a fixed personality trait. If you want to learn how to speak in public, you have to believe that your fear and timidity are not in-born characteristics that you're stuck with. If you want to explore a new career that challenges you to learn skills and knowledge that you've struggled with in the past, like math for instance, you have to believe you're capable of learning and that your intelligence in that area is not fixed.

Locus of Control

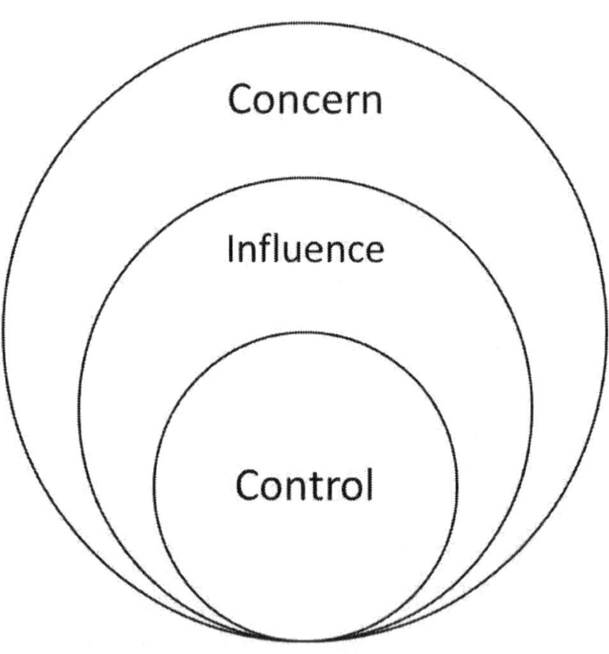

When we try to create a new story, one of the most important things is to focus on the things that we can control. Too often we waste time and energy on things that are outside of our control and influence, when we could be spending it on creating our new story. In fact, this is why many people never create their new story—they are focused on changing the wrong things. We need to direct our focus on things we CAN control—things within our "circle of control".

There are 3 levels of influence:

1. Things that you can directly control
2. Things you can influence
3. Things that you have no control and influence. So let us look at those things.

Things you CAN control:

It's important to recognize that our perception of what we can control strongly influences what we do and what we feel about situations in our life. The perception of how much control you have in your life is called "Locus of Control."

A person who has a predominant internal locus of control believes that they can (or should be able to) influence all of the events and outcomes in their life. On the other hand, someone who has a predominantly external locus of control tends to blame the outside world for nearly all things that happen in their life. As you can probably see, being at the extreme end of both of these tendencies can have a negative impact on your life. For example, someone with a high internal locus of control tends to blame himself or herself, and beat themselves up, when something does not go their way, even if they had no control of the outcome. In other words, it is important to recognize that there are things that we do not have control over. On the other hand, someone with a high external locus of control tends not to take responsibility for anything, blaming everyone else for things that are clearly within their control. They don't take control of their life because they do not think that they have the power to make the difference. People with a balanced locus of control have a realistic view of what they do have power over.

Below is a small list of things that you do have control over right now:

- How much effort you put into something
- How many times you smile, say "thank you", or show appreciation today
- How well you prepare for something
- How you react to an emotion
- What you focus on
- How you interpret a situation
- What you commit to doing or not doing
- What conversations you have and what you engage in
- How much you focus on the present moment
- What you tell yourself and how nice you are to YOU
- How you take care of your body
- How many new things you are exposed to
- What you do in your free time

- Whom you spend your time with and who your friends are
- What information you consume: courses you read, media you listen to or watch
- When you ask for help
- Whether you make plans and act on them
- How much you believe what other people say
- How long it takes you to try again when you fail

This is just a small list of examples. However, notice that all of these items are DIRECTLY related to YOU. Yes, YOU, your actions, thoughts, emotions, beliefs and choices are what are within your circle of control.

Remember that some of the things that you have control over have consequences, but those consequences do not take away from the fact that you have a choice.

What are things that do you have control over that you would want to change and take charge of?

How will taking control help you create your new story?

Things you CAN influence:

Outside of your circle of control, the next level is your sphere of influence. Our influence and perceived influence is critical to our wellbeing. In fact, researchers, Dr. Sommer and Dr. Bourgeois have been able to show that the more influential you feel you are, the greater your happiness and wellbeing. This is because feeling that we influence others gives us a sense of purpose, meaning, and control. Notice that influence is different than control. Influence does not mean telling people what to do or making them do something. That does not lead to happiness. And, the truth is that you CAN'T make people do anything.

There are two ways that you can increase your level of happiness when it comes to our influence.

1. **Increase your influence on others around you.** The type of influence we're talking about here is being a leader in our inner circle—meaning leading by example. For example, when we follow our dreams, stand up for what we believe, and when we grow, we empower other around us to do the same thing. It is about living in the reality that if you change your behavior, or attitude, other people tend to notice and are affected by those changes whether they want to or not.
2. **Increasing your awareness of how you currently influence those around you.** When you acknowledge the positive impact you are having on others, it boosts your confidence.

Influence is a normal part of human nature. It's up to you to decide in what ways you are influenced by others and whether you are a good influence on those around you. The sphere of influence goes both ways because the people that you may have influence over also influence you. Choose who you are around wisely, and be aware of the impact you have on others.

Make a list of those closest to you whom you influence and/or who influence you:	How do you influence them (both negatively and positively)?	How can you become a better positive influence on them?	How do they influence you (both positively and negatively)?	Can you replace any of your negative influences with positive ones?

Becoming a positive influencer will increase your happiness and wellbeing. Living your new story will serve as an empowering example for others. But keep an eye out for the negative influencers in your life that may hinder the story that you are trying to create.

You Can Change Your Brain

Everyone knows that when you lift weights repeatedly over time, your muscles grow bigger and get stronger. And, when you stop exercising the muscles, they shrink again and get weaker. Most people don't know that when they practice any activity and learn new information, their brain changes and gets stronger, much like a muscle.

Understanding Neuroplasticity and Why It Matters

The brain is made up of billions of tiny nerve cells called neurons that all connect together through a network of over a trillion tiny branches (made up of dendrites the receivers, and axons the transmitters). Every time we think or act, it is because these neurons are communicating by sending signals through their dendrites, all the way to whatever locations are needed to trigger the cells to act. The signal itself is a chemical called a neurotransmitter. These signals are responsible for every step you take, for your heart beating, and for thoughts and emotions.

You may have heard the phrase "neurons that fire together, wire together". What this means is that certain neurons connect to each other through chains in the network or pathways from one area of your brain to another. When you use a certain pathway or "wire" repeatedly, the connection between the neurons strengthens. The process is called myelination and it literally involves growing a protective coating that encases the wire like the rubber coating on an electric wire. This myelin sheath makes signals able to move faster, which the brain loves because it's primary goal is efficiency.

So, when you repeat a behavior, an action, an emotion, or a thought over and over again, the pathway responsible for sending the signal becomes stronger and it becomes easier and easier. This is how skills are developed and habits are formed. It's also how emotional triggers are created and negative patterns are formed. Whether the outcome is good or bad, whatever that you do repeatedly changes the physical workings of the neural connections in your brain.

But interestingly, scientists have found that because of this process the brain literally grows bigger, just like a muscle—not in size but in weight.

And what's important to know is that for many years scientists believed that the brain loses its ability to grow and change early in life, but they now have proof that even old brains can change by developing more connections and strengthening wires.

The Truth about Smart and Dumb

Most people believe that everyone's intelligence is fixed. You're born smart, dumb, or average and your capacity for learning is determined by what you're born with. But interestingly no one thinks babies are stupid because they can't talk or read or solve equations. Those things, of course, are all learned with practice and exposure. And, babies can't walk until their muscles get stronger. We don't question this, but somehow, we've been tricked into believing that after a certain point, you're either smart or not and that's the end of it.

But the truth is that, while there are minor variations between people with innate predispositions, the factor that contributes to a person's level of intelligence at any age is their exposure to information and experience combined with the amount of time they spend learning.

The truth is that intelligence can be grown just like any physical capability can be improved. It takes work and it can be challenging, but this is also the case for a weightlifter who wants to increase their strength or a runner who wants to increase their speed.

So, now you know that you can change and grow your brain. When you practice a new skill over and over again or you increase your exposure to new experiences repeatedly, your brain grows stronger in those related areas. People who play an instrument have increased brain activity in the area of their brain related to their hands. People who drive cabs have a larger hippocampus than everyone else, which is the area of the brain responsible for spatial memory. So, whatever you spend more of your time and energy doing will grow your brain in the corresponding area. But it's not just repeating something that makes you learn and grow, it is DELIBERATELY learning how to get better at it. What unlocks the door to true growth is learning a new tool, strategy, or insight that helps you do something BETTER—not simply doing more of the same old thing.

And that's why, in this course, we're going to provide tools, strategies, and insights for changing your thoughts and behaviors. You'll develop your awareness of the thoughts and emotions that go on in your mind and body. You'll learn strategies for recognizing patterns and identifying underlying beliefs that influence what you think and do. You'll learn how thought works and what's going on inside your brain and body when you experience emotions so that you can understand how these thoughts and feelings cause you to behave the way you do.

The human brain is the most amazing and powerful tool in the world and you are blessed to have one. It may not have come with an owners' manual, but now that you know how it works you have the power to use this tool to change your life.

Common Misperceptions about the Growth Mindset

When learning about the growth mindset for the first time, there are several common misperceptions that can prevent you from being able to develop a true growth mindset, either because you reject the idea because you feel like having a fixed mindset makes you wrong or bad or because you struggle to identify authentic growth mindset from simply the appearance of it.

First, no one is either 100% fixed or 100% growth oriented. Everyone is on a spectrum between the two. In addition, someone can be fixed in one area of their life, such as believing their intelligence is fixed, but have a growth mindset in other areas, such as believing they can develop their singing ability.

Second, people's life situation can impact how they view themselves and others. For example, you could have a growth mindset that help you achieve success within your organization and then be promoted to leadership position and then start believing that you have all the answers and fall into a fix mind set. More than anything, it's important to know that everyone's mindset changes over their life.

Third, being positive or open minded does not mean someone has a growth mindset. Also, people who learn about a growth mindset who lean more toward a fixed mindset may try to take on qualities they believe growth mindset people have, even thought they are still seeing from a fixed perspective. It's important for fixed mindset people to remind themselves (or for you to remind them) that it takes practice and time to learn a new way of viewing the world. There is nothing wrong with them, in fact, it's extremely common! But the good news is that they can change.

Fourth, it is easy to get the idea that growth mindset people don't care about outcomes, only effort. But it's not that positive outcomes are not valued or rewarded, it's that the effort is valued and rewarded more. And, effort that doesn't eventually lead to progress is not rewarded either. The goal is learning and progress, not just effort. Effort that doesn't result in progress over time is wasted effort. If a low performing employee is not learning from their mistakes, even after support, they may not be a good fit for that position.

Mindset Assessment

There are no right or wrong answers. Choose the option that best fits you.

I believe I can always change my talent, no matter how much I have to start with.

- 1 Strongly Disagree
- 2 Disagree
- 3 Disagree Somewhat
- 4 Agree Somewhat
- 5 Agree
- 6 Strongly Agree

I like working on things that make me think hard.

- 1 Strongly Disagree
- 2 Disagree
- 3 Disagree Somewhat
- 4 Agree Somewhat
- 5 Agree
- 6 Strongly Agree

I don't mind making a lot of errors when I first start learning something new.

- 1 Strongly Disagree
- 2 Disagree
- 3 Disagree Somewhat
- 4 Agree Somewhat
- 5 Agree
- 6 Strongly Agree

When something is hard, it makes me want to try harder. It doesn't make me want to give up.

- 1 Strongly Disagree
- 2 Disagree
- 3 Disagree Somewhat
- 4 Agree Somewhat
- 5 Agree
- 6 Strongly Agree

I know I can learn new things, but I don't believe I can change my intelligence.

- 6 Strongly Disagree
- 5 Disagree
- 4 Disagree Somewhat
- 3 Agree Somewhat
- 2 Agree
- 1 Strongly Agree

I prefer doing things that I can do well at without putting a lot of effort into it.

- 6 Strongly Disagree
- 5 Disagree
- 4 Disagree Somewhat
- 3 Agree Somewhat
- 2 Agree
- 1 Strongly Agree

I prefer to work on things that I can do perfectly or get right most of the time.

- 6 Strongly Disagree
- 5 Disagree
- 4 Disagree Somewhat
- 3 Agree Somewhat
- 2 Agree
- 1 Strongly Agree

If I have to try hard or put in extra work, it makes me feel like I'm not good enough.

- 6 Strongly Disagree
- 5 Disagree
- 4 Disagree Somewhat
- 3 Agree Somewhat
- 2 Agree
- 1 Strongly Agree

Add up the numbers that correspond to each of your answers. **Your Score:** ________________

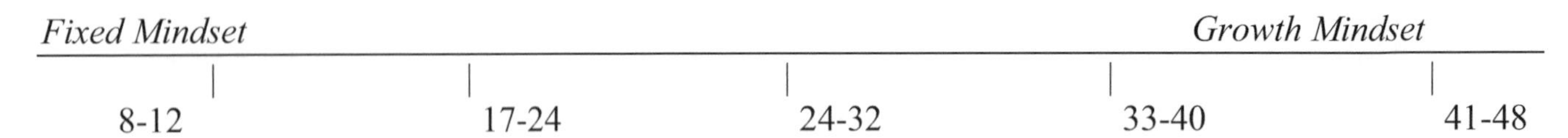

What it Means

8-12: You strongly believe that your talents, intelligence, and abilities are fixed traits that can't be changed. You see putting in effort and trying hard as a sign that you just aren't good at what you're doing. If you are not likely to do well or succeed, you would rather not participate and instead choose to do things that come easy for you. You believe that talented or highly intelligent people are that way naturally and they do not have to put in effort to be that way.

17-24: You believe your talents, intelligence, and abilities probably don't change very much. You tend to choose situations in which you don't make many mistakes and you don't have to put in too much effort. You believe that learning and improving should be easy to do.

25-32: You're not sure if your talents, intelligence, or abilities can be changed, but you recognize you can learn and change in some ways. You care about your performance and being good at things, but you also value learning something new that you're not as good at, yet. You prefer not to have to try too hard.

33-40: You believe you can increase your intelligence and improve your talents and abilities. You care about learning and growing, and you're not afrait to put in effort to improve. You care about performing well, but you value learning, too. You would never avoid doing something in order to avoid looking or being bad at it.

41-48: You strongly believe that you can learn, grow, and improve in all areas, including your talents, intelligence, and abilities. You enjoy being challenged by things you're not good at, yet. You believe in the value of hard work, you don't fear making mistakes, looking bad, or even failing because you know these things lead you to learn and improve. You value performing very well and therefore you value the effort and learning it takes to succeed.

Remember: Your mindset can change and develop! You can shift your mindset more toward a growth mindset. Find out more at www.mindsetworks.com.

Developing a Growth Mindset Step 1: Awareness

Now that you know what a growth mindset is and why it is such an important belief system, you can begin to practice this way of thinking.

Awareness of Your Self-Talk and Fixed Mindset Triggers

Everyone has an internal voice, and part of this voice is an inner critic, inner hater, or inner doubter—it is the fixed mindset persona. You can hear this persona within the negative self-talk that happens in your thoughts and mind. It can sound like:

- I'm not good enough.
- I will probably fail.
- I can't do this.
- I don't want to risk it.
- I shouldn't have to try so hard.
- If I'm not naturally good at this, I should just quit.
- It's not my fault.
- This makes me uncomfortable, I'm not doing it.
- Why try if it won't change anything?

What does yours often sound like?

Give your fixed mindset persona a name. Naming it helps you remind yourself that this mindset—or habit of thinking—is not who you are!

I will call my fixed mindset persona: ______________________________

Identify your triggers. What situations tend to trigger your fixed mindset persona?

- When you're thinking about taking on a big challenge or learning something new?

  ☐ always ☐ sometimes ☐ never

  What does your fixed mindset persona tell you when you're in this situation?

- When you're thinking about making a change?

  ☐ always ☐ sometimes ☐ never

  What does your fixed mindset persona tell you when you're in this situation?

- When someone criticizes you?

  ☐ always ☐ sometimes ☐ never

  What does your fixed mindset persona tell you when you're in this situation?

- When you fail at something?

  ☐ always ☐ sometimes ☐ never

  What does your fixed mindset persona tell you when you're in this situation?

- When something goes wrong? Do you beat yourself up or blame someone else?

  ☐ always ☐ sometimes ☐ never

  What does your fixed mindset persona tell you when you're in this situation?

- When someone else makes a mistake? Do you judge them? Criticism them?

  ☐ always ☐ sometimes ☐ never

  What does your fixed mindset persona tell you when you're in this situation?

- When you're under pressure or on a deadline?

  ☐ always ☐ sometimes ☐ never

  What does your fixed mindset persona tell you when you're in this situation?

- When you procrastinate or are feeling lazy?

  ☐ always ☐ sometimes ☐ never

  What does your fixed mindset persona tell you when you're in this situation?

- When you have a conflict with someone?

  ☐ always ☐ sometimes ☐ never

  What does your fixed mindset persona tell you when you're in this situation?

- When your reputation is at risk or you worry what others will think?

  ☐ always ☐ sometimes ☐ never

  What does your fixed mindset persona tell you when you're in this situation?

Awareness of Your Reaction

Ask yourself, how am I rationalizing or judging the situation?

How am I beating myself up or blaming others?

What is the fixed mindset telling me?

Developing a Growth Mindset Part 2: Perspective

You may not always be able to change what happens around you, but you always have a choice of how you respond, react, and how you view the situation.

When you catch your fixed mindset persona with a limited thought, ask yourself, what else might be going on here?

What is a more realistic and optimistic way to look at this situation?

What are the good aspects of this situation?

How can I look at this differently?

Here are examples of rephrasing fixed mindset thinking as growth mindset thinking. Be on the lookout for any time you hear your fixed mindset persona taking over your internal dialogue, such as the reactions to the triggers you identified or the following common fixed mindset thoughts, you can change your perspective to a growth mindset,

- When you hear yourself thinking something like: "What if you're not good enough? You'll be a failure."
  Change it to: "Everyone starts out not being good and successful people all fail along the way."
- When you hear yourself thinking: "If it's this hard, you're probably just not good at it."
  Change it to: "If it's hard, it means I need to put in more effort and it will be a great achievement when I get good at it."
- When you hear yourself thinking: "If I don't try, I can't fail and I will keep my dignity."
  Change it to: "If I don't try, I have already failed and I have no dignity."
- When you hear yourself thinking: "It's not my fault."
  Change it to: "If I don't accept whatever part of this is my responsibility, I give away my power."

Go back through the fixed mindset triggers you identified and what your persona tends to tell you and rewrite a NEW thought from the growth mindset perspective.

My fixed mindset trigger thought:

My replacement growth mindset perspective:

My fixed mindset trigger thought:

My replacement growth mindset perspective:

My fixed mindset trigger thought:

My replacement growth mindset perspective:

My fixed mindset trigger thought:

My replacement growth mindset perspective:

Developing a Growth Mindset Part 3: Action

So, at this point you've noticed your fixed mindset persona thinking limited thoughts and you've changed your perspective. The next step is the most important, and in fact is what truly makes someone have a growth mindset. The most important factor for developing a growth mindset is action.

As yourself, what did you learn from the experience?

What could you do differently next time or going forward?

What would help you achieve this goal that you haven't tried?

What do you need to learn or what information do you need to gather?

What steps will you take?

DON'T STOP THERE! List out the steps that you will take, and for each one, identify exactly WHEN you will do it. If anything on your list cannot happen within 1 week, save it for later and re-assess at the end of the week. For everything else, include when you will do it and what you need in order to do it.

Lastly, **take 5 minutes to visualize yourself** taking each of these steps, as you imagine they will play out, including achieving the goal and outcome you are aiming for.

Practicing a Growth Mindset

Select your favorite affirmations from the list below or write your own and put them somewhere you will see them every day, such as next to your bed, on your mirror, on the cover of your day planner, attached to your computer screen, or programmed into the calendar of your phone to remind you to look at them every day, at least once.

- Everyone has a fixed mindset to some degree. Now that I know the difference and I know I can change, I am developing a growth mindset.
- Challenges, risks, and failures do not reflect that I am a failure, they are opportunities for me to grow and improve.
- I care more about the process and the journey and who I become along the way than I do about the outcome.

- I am glad that I am not perfect and that I never will be because it means I am not limited to where I am today.
- What other people think about me is none of my business. I no longer allow other people's opinions and judgments to hold me back from living a life of fulfillment and reaching my potential.
- I am always looking for the meaning and lessons contained in all situations that can help me fulfill the greater purpose in my life.
- I move past the discomfort of making mistakes quickly because I learn the lesson and allow it to help me improve so I can do better next time.
- I know that no one starts out great at something and so I am willing to try new things and practice skills I would like to have, putting in the time and effort I know it takes to master this area.
- I am the master of my thoughts, emotions, and actions and I do not give my power away by reacting to others criticism, judgment, or actions in a negative way.
- Having to exert effort in order to be good at something is a good thing because it shows me that I am capable of learning and improving. I love knowing I am not limited to my current strengths.
- I love knowing that even if someone else may be more naturally talented in an area than I am, a person with better work ethic will out perform a person with talent every time.
- I know that most truly successful people have failed their way to success.
- I have skills and knowledge today that I didn't have before because I learned and grew in those areas, so I know I can develop any ability I want.
- If my talents, abilities, and intelligence are not fixed, this means my potential is truly limitless!

Write your own:

Understanding Cognition (How Thinking Works)

Thoughts Create Emotions and Behaviors

As we've established, CBT is based on the premise that our thoughts create our emotions and influence our behavior. The 3 aspects—thoughts, emotions, behaviors—interplay and influence each other, however the area where we have the most power is our thoughts because they are almost always the foundation of our emotions and the behaviors that we take because of them. The good news, which is why CBT is so powerful, is that because we can learn to have greater control over our thoughts, we can have greater control over our emotions and our behaviors.

As discussed in the "What is CBT" section, cognition includes the processes of thinking as well as processing an experience, including what is taken in by the 5 senses. When you experience anything in life, it is interpreted by your brain, which means in a split second your brain compares what it is taking in through your senses, which tells it what is going on in your experience, to everything else you've ever experienced. It's trying to make a snap judgment of:

- What is going on
- What it means
- How you should feel about it
- What you should do

The brain has evolved to rapidly interpret everything you experience and it's so good at it that you don't even notice it's happening. That is, until something happens that causes your mind to interpret a situation as negative. It chooses a perspective or belief about the situation that creates an emotional reaction in your body. It's unpleasant, so it's noticeable. Your body reacts to this emotion, which is actually caused by the thought triggering your body to release any of a number of brain chemicals, often referred to as neurotransmitters or endorphins or hormones. Your brain is like a chemical factory and there is a different neurotransmitter that is responsible for every emotion you can feel.

It all functions as it should. Something threatens you, your brain interprets, triggers the hormones that shoot throughout your body inspiring you spring into action. Someone tells you they adore you and you're flooded with feel-good chemicals. Our bodies and brain are amazing machines. But sometimes, these emotional reactions get out of whack with what's actually happening. You can feel anxious for no reason. Something small makes you furious. You're sad even when you're doing something that usually makes you happy.

What's happened is that your mind has learned a pattern of thinking that is faulty. Your brain is interpreting situations negatively, when they're not. Your mind is judging situations, or yourself. You have unconscious limiting beliefs impacting your perspective that you aren't aware of. Your brain was doing what it does best—trying to interpret your world in a way that protects you. Unfortunately, as you lived life, your brain got programmed by the world around you. Your thoughts were influenced by the actions of others. Your core beliefs were adopted from the beliefs of others. And because you weren't aware of any of this, your mind became trapped by its own faulty beliefs. Your thoughts run amok and you were never taught how to catch them.

It happens to everyone. Humans bodies and brains don't come with an owners' manual! But the good news is that the solution is simple. You can become more aware of this process. You can change your thought patterns and beliefs. You can reprogram yourself. You can become conscious of your unconscious thoughts and behaviors. You can choose to experience more positive emotions, and less negative ones.

You have this power to control your own mind—a power that has been withheld from you your entire life. And it's time to take your power back!

Let's Look at Emotions

The best place to start a discussion about how thinking works and impacts your life is to look at emotions. Let me ask you a question, should emotions be trusted?

Some people say, "You should always trust your emotions."

Other people say, "Feelings are irrational and can't be trusted."

So, which is it?

They're BOTH wrong.

Emotions and feelings are neither right nor wrong, accurate or not. Emotions are simply your body's reaction to what you are THINKING. Your belief system and other unconscious thoughts are happening on autopilot all the time, and cause emotions. That's why sometimes you have NO IDEA why you feel the way you do.

So, here's an example of why emotions are never either right or wrong… because they're just reacting to your thoughts…

Think about something that you really, really wish you had, but that you don't have.

You may feel unhappy because you don't have it, but that's not true. You are unhappy because of the THOUGHT of not having it.

Let me prove it to you:

Have you ever been happy while not having this thing you want? __Yes __No

If you didn't have it but you didn't care that you didn't have it, could you be unhappy? __Yes __No

If you didn't have it but were doing something else that kept you from thinking about it, such as going down a roller coaster, would you be unhappy about it? No.

You see, not having what you want doesn't make you feel bad.

Thinking about it does.

Where Do Emotions Come From?

Sometimes our unconscious mind and senses are picking up cues from our environment that trigger emotions, such as reading a person's body language or facial expression and having an automatic physiological response or sensing danger and having an automatic fear response. (By the way, to learn more about the fight-or-flight response that causes you to feel fear and anxiety, check out the Situational vs Psychological Fear section in the Developing Awareness section.)

However, most of the time it is NOT the outside world or the situation that is happening that causes our emotional reaction—it's what we're thinking. It is the mental filter that the situation passes through—aka, our interpretation—that then causes our emotional reaction to the situation.

Situation → Interpretation (Thought) → Emotion

The key to understand here is that research over decades on CBT provides evidence that we can have control over our thoughts. And if we have control over our thoughts, we can control our emotions. It may be challenging to do this, but it is a skill that can be learned. Here's the process:

Recognize Emotion→ Identify Thought → Change Thought → Change Emotion

Changing the Thought

Once you notice that a thought is happening it becomes conscious. Since you're aware of it, you can then choose to change it. Your mind automatically interpreted the situation, but now that you're paying attention to it you can choose a different interpretation—a different perspective. This is great news because when you change the way you look at things, the things you look at change. Even in the same situation or with the same facts, if you change your viewpoint, your experience of the situation will change. Here is an example: a man was visiting a friend's house and went into the kitchen to make some tea. He didn't find a tea kettle, and so poured water into a glass coffee carafe and placed it on the gas stove. He returned to the living room and minute later smelled something burning. He returned and found that the handle of the carafe had caught fire. He quickly put the fire out. He apologized to his friend and was feeling both embarrassed and guilty. His friend, however, was laughing and complemented him on his "fireman" skills. Same situation, different perspectives—and the result was completely different emotional responses.

Why this matters!

So, this matters because, of course, you want to feel better. If you change your perspective of a situation, you will change your emotional reaction to it. But it's even better than that!

You see, your emotions are the driving force for your BEHAVIORS because the decisions you make are based on how you feel. As you get better at being aware of your emotions and thinking, you'll be able to make decisions from a place of control—you might feel a certain way, but you'll use your cognitive processes to choose to act from a place of rational thought.

But if you're like most people, you're not at that place yet—at least not all the time.

So, here's where we are now:

Thought → Emotion → Decisions → Action/Behaviors

The behaviors you exhibit and the actions you take are a direct result of your thoughts. So, if you are experiencing behaviors you don't like or have been doing things you aren't pleased with, your thoughts are to blame.

If you can't yet see the behaviors or actions you're doing that aren't serving you, look around at your life at the results you're experiencing. Have you been having any problems at work or in your relationships? Have you experienced anything unpleasant? Are there are things you want that you don't have? On the positive side, what aspects of your life have you managed to create that you want, enjoy, or love?

The reason I ask is because I'm going to take this cause and effect train one more step.

Thought → Emotion → Decisions → Action/Behaviors → Results/Outcomes

That's right, your behaviors and actions are what determine the results and outcomes you experience in your life—both the wanted ones and the unwanted ones.

By changing your thoughts, you can literally transform your life. Literally! So, let's dive into more about understanding how thinking works.

Cognitive Distortions

CBT techniques are designed to help people overcome their faulty programming. We all have common ways that our thought processes are dysfunctional, called cognitive distortions. These inaccurate thoughts reinforce negative thinking patterns and emotions and convince us of a reality that is simply not true. It can be liberating just hearing about these distortions because once you recognize that the reality you assume isn't necessarily 100% accurate, you can open up to greater possibilities! Even people who pride themselves on being critical thinkers can get stuck in these traps.

All-or-Nothing / Polarized Thinking: This distortion is also known as "Black-and-White Thinking," and it occurs when a person is not able to see the gray areas of any situations. In other words, the person may not be able to or willing to see that there may be other factors or different options in any situation. Therefore, they stay stuck between two extremes which makes them hard to compromise with others or make a decision. For example, If everything is either perfect or awful there is not room for all the emotions and experiences that can be in between. Another example may be a person that fails in something may think that they are a total failure without recognizing that they may need to improve in an area in their life and that the single failure does not define them and their capabilities.

Overgeneralization: In this distortion a person overgeneralizes things in their life, such as defining a single occurrence as an overall pattern. For example, a person may have a misunderstanding while communicating with a friend and then assume that they are just bad at communicating with everyone. They may even generalize further and believe they are disliked by everyone. Therefore, this bias leads to negative thoughts about the person's life in general, based on one or two experiences that they feel defines them. In others words, a single incident is used as evidence to conclude something. The biggest challenge with overgeneralizing is that we may define our abilities or characteristics based one experience and then stop trying in future situations because if that one experience.

Jumping to Conclusions: (Making assumptions or mind reading.) This distortion happens when we assume what the other person is thinking, or what their intentions are. It is true that at times we may have a general idea of why a person may do something, but we usually don't acknowledge that our assumptions may be erroneous. Therefore, we may see someone and their nonverbal reaction and assume that they may not be interested in what we have to say when they may actually simply be distracted with something else in their life. We may even think that they are thinking something negative about us when that the truth may be far from that reality. Our predictions and conclusions are typically based on our own biases instead of reality. We may even conclude that our fear may come true and avoid a situation before we have a chance to find out.

Magnification (Catastrophizing) or Minimization: This distortion is when you exaggerate the meaning of something, or on the other extreme you minimize it. For example, a person may make a mistake at work and may magnify that mistake to make it seem like they will ruin the project that the company is working on. At the same time a person may get an award for something and minimize it and still believe that they are still not good enough. This leads people to always look at worst case scenarios.

Emotional Reasoning: This is an important distortion that people must identify and address because it's common. Emotional reasoning is when we take our emotions as a fact. In other words, if we feel it then it must be true, and we find reasons to justify it. For example, if we feel dumb or unattractive in our current moment then we believe it must be an overall fact of who we are. We feel that way, therefore it's real. However, the truth is that our emotional state in a given moment on a specific topic is rarely indicative of reality. Unfortunately, for many it is difficult to see past their current emotional state.

Should Statements: Another common distortion is "should" statements. You may have noticed times when you are telling yourself that you should do this, should not do that, or must do this other thing. The truth about should statements is that they are almost always based on what we think others around us believe we should do, rather than what we truly want. The problem is we often create "shoulds" and expectations for ourselves that are unrealistic and hard to meet and then beat up ourselves and feel guilty because of them. And worse, we don't even actually believe them and we're doing it for everyone else. This leads to us making decisions that don't benefit us short term or long term. At the same time, we also place shoulds and expectations on others and when they do not meet our requirements it may lead to anger and resentment.

Labeling and Mislabeling: This is another form of overgeneralizing—a tendency to assign a judgment or label based on a single event or instance. We allow the event to define ourselves or others. If you're golfing and you miss your put and lose, you tell yourself "I'm a loser" instead of simply "I goofed this one up." This happened, and therefore I am that. You can also label others. For instance, if you meet someone that does not say hello right away you may label them as a mean person who does not like you, when in reality the person may have been distracted and it had nothing to do with you. Not only did you assume the person's intentions, you judged and labeled them. With labeling, you're overgeneralizing a single trait as the main definition of yourself or others. Mislabeling is when you apply a label that is not just overgeneralized, it is inaccurate and usually uses highly emotional and exaggerated language.

Personalization: This distortion is also a common one that many people can relate to and have experience at some point of their life. It involves us taking things personally and blaming ourselves for something in an illogical way. For instance, you may believe someone is acting a certain way because of you when it has nothing to do with you. In extreme cases you may assume that you are the cause of the moods or behaviors of those around us. When bad things happen around you, you think it's your fault. For example, if you are late to a meeting and then the meeting is a disaster, you may tell yourself that everything would have been fine if you were early, when the reality is that the outcome had nothing to do with you.

Blaming: On the other end of the spectrum from people who personalize everything, there are the people that never take responsibilities for their action. This fallacy of blaming leads us to blame others for what goes wrong, and not just the outcomes—we even blame others for our emotions, thoughts, and behavior without realizing that we can always choose our emotions and behaviors.

Fallacy of Fairness: This is another common fallacy. We would all like to believe that life is fair however, reality is that life can be unfair at times. Unfairness can cause negative emotions. Some people may find themselves judging a situation based on whether something is fair or not, rather than looking at the objective reality, which will only lead to anger, resentment, and hopelessness. Therefore, it's important to come to acceptance that some things will go our way and some things won't and that we can always choose to make the best of any situation instead of judging it, which adds another layer of stress or anger. Another aspect of this is the "just world hypothesis" which is the belief that the world is just and, therefore, if something bad happens to someone it has to be because they deserved it, they are bad. This can lead people to judge, reject, and blame others because of the bad things that happen to that person—even if it is clearly not their fault. People also judge, reject, and blame themselves and when bad things happen to them, they believe it means they are bad.

Fallacy of Change: This is the belief and expectation that we can change others to meet our needs. A person experiencing this may put pressure on others and attempt to force them to meet his or her needs. Not only do they believe others can or will change and bend to their will, which they won't, the main issue is the belief that their own success and happiness depends on other people being what they want them to be and meeting their needs. This leads to a lack of taking personal responsibility for meeting their own needs and causes resentment for both parties when the attempts at forcing someone to change are unsuccessful.

Always Being Right: People who tend to be perfectionists may experience this. This is the belief that we must be right or correct. Therefore, being wrong is unacceptable and we will do whatever we must to prove that we are right, even when we are wrong. Agreeing to disagree does not exist in those people's world and they may have destructive relationships, since they try to be right at all cost. Many times, they are also unable to admit mistakes, be fair, or be open to other views or beliefs.

Heaven's Reward Fallacy: This is the belief system that suffering and hard work is what will lead to a just reward. This may lead to some creating unnecessary suffering in their life. It can also lead to people getting frustrated when their hard work or suffering does not lead to the expected results. Sometimes no matter how hard you work on something or how much you suffer through a situation it will not lead to a reward or to achieve what you thought you would achieve. We can also think of it from the perspective of Karma and assume that if we do good that a reward or something good must occur. Good may occur, but if it does not meet our expectations or people do not react in ways that we expect, we may feel frustrated, angry and even depressed.

Mental Filter: Mental filters are very similar to overgeneralization. This is where a person may focus completely on one thing, such as the negative aspect of a situation, without being able to see the other sides, the positives. For example, a person may have a conversation and hear one negative thing that the other person said and then neglect to recognize or remember all the positive things that the person said. This tendency can lead us to only focus on the negative things around us. This can also happen if we have a bad thing happen to us in the morning and then expect that we are going to have a bad day because of it. We then filter out everything good in our day and only focus on negative things, which in the end proves our prediction correct and makes us feel like our bad morning ruined the whole day.

Disqualifying the Positive: On the other side we have disqualifying the positives, and this is when we do recognize the positive but instead of accepting them we reject them. For example, if someone gives you a compliment, instead of accepting it we may feel that the person is just saying it to be nice to us and that they do not really mean it. This can lead us to develop a negative though habit in which we focus on the negatives even when positives are present or when we are presented with things that counter the negative.

Stop Irrational and Illogical Thinking with Socratic Questioning

The truth is that we all think illogically or irrationally sometimes. I'm sure you know people who say things that you really wonder to yourself "how could they possibly think that?" Or, maybe you've had an argument with someone and it feels like you're spinning in circles or that you're talking to a brick wall. This happens because it's easy to get locked into a thinking pattern that doesn't make any sense. But the truth is that sometimes the person who is stuck in illogical thinking is YOU. Something can make so much sense to us at the time, but then someone points something out or you find our more information later that helps you realize that the way you were thinking about the situation made no sense.

When you're emotional, in fact, almost all thinking is irrational. The reason is that when we become emotional, our emotional center in our brain called the amygdala kicks on and floods our bodies with chemicals. At the same time, the prefrontal cortex, which is responsible for rational thought, shuts off. Our ability to think logically is literally impaired until our emotions are back under control. This is a really good reason for never making decisions when you're highly emotional AND why to never continue to talk or argue when either you or the other person is highly emotional. Nothing good will come out of it.

But sometimes, emotions aside, our thoughts are irrational because there are so many assumptions, distortions, and limited perspectives that can lead us not to be clear with our thinking. The good news is that there are ways to root out illogical thoughts, which is important because if our thoughts impact our emotions and actions we don't want to be creating our life experience based on thoughts that aren't even true.

This is where Socratic questioning comes in, also referred to cognitive restructuring.

Socrates is an early Greek philosopher who was one of the greatest thinkers of all time. He was famous for his ability to prove that someone else's thinking was illogical. The person would state their opinion and then Socrates would ask them questions until he led the person to make a statement that contradicted their original claim, showing that their original opinion was illogical.

The philosophy behind this type of questioning is that disciplined questioning can help a person uncover the truth, expand their thinking, uncover assumptions, and follow a line of thought all the way through. You'll notice that this type of questioning is used in a number of activities throughout the program.

Thoughts are going on inside our minds all the time like a running dialog. They happen fast and we often aren't really aware they're happening. We have an entire section dedicated to developing awareness, but to start use this activity to begin tune into your thoughts. The attachment that goes with this section helps you use Socratic questioning on yourself to determine if what you are thinking is logical.

These questions will help you develop a greater understanding of WHY you think what you think and whether the thought is rational and logical. Then, later in the course we'll look at how to use this type of questioning to question underlying belief systems.

Socratic Questions

What is the thought you would like to question?

What evidence is there that this thought is true?

What evidence is there that is might not be true?

Is this evidence based on facts or your feelings?

Is your thinking black and white or all-or-nothing? Is the situation more complex than what you are assuming?

Could you be misinterpreting the evidence or making any unverified assumptions?

Would other people have different interpretations of the same situation? If so, what might they think?

Are you looking at ALL relevant evidence, not looking only at the evidence that supports what you already believe?

Are you exaggerating or thinking this way just because it's your habit?

Where did this thought came from? Who may have passed it onto you? Are they a valuable source?

Why Journaling is the Core of CBT

Journaling is an essential process for developing a better understanding ourselves and why we do what we do. Journaling helps us investigate and dig deeper, gather data and information, and then reflect.

The processes used in CBT will uncover thought and behavioral patterns, identify and change irrational beliefs, generate insights into the cause of behaviors, and explore possibilities for creating change. However, the key that unlocks this ability is WRITING EVERYTHING DOWN. Thoughts that aren't recorded cannot be evaluated. Insights that aren't recorded will be forgotten. Changes cannot be made unless they are understood. And this is why journaling is the core process used for CBT.

This style of journaling is highly focused, meaning what is being written is very specific. Rather than free writing, this journaling focuses specifically on recording thoughts, emotions and behaviors. The goal is to develop awareness of how our thoughts, emotions, and behaviors relate to each other and what causes them, and then to use what is learned to make changes that impact behavior, and therefore, results.

By tracking your experiences, you will begin to see thought patterns, emotional tendencies, and behavior patterns and how they connect. By recording these behaviors and reflecting on what is going on in your mind and your experience, you'll determine which came first, the chicken (the thought) or the egg (the behavior). Actually, you'll find that there is usually a string of cause and effect. Once you can see the patterns, you can change them. You'll be taking mental processes that are happening unconsciously, meaning below your level of awareness, and pulling them into your conscious mind. We'll explore how to develop your awareness of these thoughts and emotions in the Developing Awareness section.

The ABCDEF Journaling Process

All of the different elements of irrational thinking and beliefs that we've learned about can be summed up in one belief: "I am supposed to always get what I want and feel the way I want, and other people and the world must meet these demands."

Deep down what we're really trying to do is keep ourselves safe, be loved, and feel good about ourselves. The underlying drive behind all of this is natural and healthy—but because sometimes our needs aren't met and we don't feel safe or loved or good about ourselves our brains have to try to explain why. We believe that even just the thought that we might not get what we want is cause for concern. The first thing our brain tries to do is to control everything in life. This is where our demanding beliefs come from. The brain believes that if we establish an absolute rule that our needs will be met, we can force life into submission.

But of course, it doesn't work. When these demands are not met, our brain needs to explain WHY the rules were broken and our needs weren't met. Unfortunately, instead of recognizing that the core belief that everything is supposed to be perfect and under our control is WRONG, it develops new beliefs to explain the problem. These beliefs are usually one of these three things:

1. I am bad or unworthy.
2. They are bad or unworthy.
3. This is the end of the world and I am a victim.

The main premise is that both the underlying rule and the judgment we make when it isn't met are UNTRUE and our demands are NEVER going to be met, and therefore this is the cause of our emotional disturbances.

So, if we can identify and change the core beliefs, we can turn our negative, unhealthy emotional disturbances into healthy emotional reactions that lead to constructive behaviors and desired outcomes. Instead of feeling like other people and the world are blocking us from reaching our goals, we can develop a belief system that helps us stop ourselves from using life circumstances as an excuse to sabotage our own success. So, how do we do this?

Step 1) First, we identify the PROBLEM by becoming aware of the dysfunctional thinking that's going on.

This has 3 steps:

A. Which stands for ACTIVATING EVENT: Something happens.
B. Which stands for BELIEF: You hold a belief about the situation.
C. Which stands for CONSEQUENCE: You have an emotional reaction and a behavioral reaction, which also lead to consequences in our lives.

It is very important to notice that the entire point that CBT is trying to make is that A does not cause C directly. A situation that happens in life is not what causes us to feel or act a certain way. It is our BELIEF about the situation that causes how we feel and act. However, often it is not obvious what belief is influencing the emotional and behavioral consequences. When working through this process, recognize that often you will need to reflect on the activating event and the emotional and behavioral consequences FIRST in order to then figure out the belief beneath them.

For example:

A. Activating Event: Your employer accuses you of taking money from the register when you didn't.
B. Belief: You believe, "She has no right to do that. She is looking for a reason to fire me!"
C. Consequences: You feel angry and take action based on how you feel, which may be to lash out, putting your job in jeopardy.

In this situation, the lashing out would be a sign that there is a rule being broken, meaning an irrational belief is leading to the unconstructive behavior.

If your belief about the situation was different, your emotional response would have been different:

A. Your employer accuses you of taking money from the register (even though you didn't).
B. You believe, "I can't lose my job!"
C. You feel anxious and take action based on how you feel, which may be shutting down and being unable to bring up your feelings with your boss.

This belief leads to a different outcome, but it is still actually an irrational belief. It may be true that you don't want to lose your job, but focusing on how terrible it would be causes anxiety which gets in the way of a successful outcome. A rational belief would be to believe "I understand that someone took money from the register and that my boss believes it was me. It is hurtful to think she believes I would do that, but it's just a misunderstanding. I can talk to her about the situation and help her understand that it was not me. I don't want to lose my job, so I want to approach this with care." Of course, you would still feel a little angry, offended, and concerned, but you wouldn't be lashing out or shutting down. You'd be experiencing healthy negative emotions and dealing with the situation with constructive behaviors.

So, the goal of the first step is to identify what is going on and then identify the problem, which is the irrational belief. The reason the belief is the problem is because it is what leads to the undesirable emotions and behaviors that lead to the undesirable negative consequence.

Step 2) Next, we dispute the irrational beliefs—this is step D.

- Challenge your thinking—is it true?

- Alternative thinking. Now that you've identified your thinking and how it impacts the situation, as well as challenged the validity of your thoughts and assumptions, you have the opportunity to choose thoughts that better serve you.
- Positive belief and affirmation. Based on the thoughts you identified, write down the core belief that is beneath them
- Action plan. What could you do differently if the situation happened again?
- Improvement. After reviewing your experience and thoughts, as well as the alternatives, how do you feel?

ABCD Journaling Worksheet

A=Activating Event

1. The situation. Briefly describe the situation, including the behavior or experience.

What was happening at the time (including who was around)?

What was the trigger?

2. Initial thought. What were you thinking about at the time?

What was the first thought that entered your mind?

How did you feel?

Which came first, the thought, the emotion, or the behavior?

Beliefs

1. Negative thinking. Identify in what ways your thoughts are negative.

Are you focusing on the negative aspects of the situation?

Are you feeling overly concerned about what other people think about you?

Are you making negative assumptions?

Next, see if you can identify one of the cognitive distortions, which we talk about in an earlier section.

- All-or-nothing thinking
- Overgeneralizations
- Jumping to conclusions
- Catastrophizing
- Minimization
- Emotional reasoning
- Should statements
- Labeling or mislabeling
- Personalization
- Blaming
- Fallacy of fairness
- Fallacy of change
- Always being right
- Heaven's reward fallacy
- Mental filter
- Disqualifying the positive

2. Source of negative belief. Based on the initial thought you identified, what made you think that?

What underlying belief or assumption was the cause?

What experience in your past caused you to believe this?

Is there a specific situation or person where you learned this?

Is there a deeper level belief or fear beneath it?

Consequence

1. If you continue to think this way, what will be the short-term consequence?

What will happen long term if you don't change your thinking?

How will it impact how you feel?

Your other thoughts?

Your behaviors or actions?

How will it impact your life?

Your relationships?

Your career?

Other areas?

Disputing

1. Challenge your thinking. Is it true?

How do you know?

Who do you know that thinks this way?

How is it working for them?

Have you been in a similar situation before?

What did you learn from it?

What advice would you give someone else in the same situation?

2. Alternative thinking. Now that you've identified your thinking and how it impacts the situation, as well as challenged the validity of your thoughts and assumptions, you have the opportunity to choose thoughts that better serve you. (See Developing Awareness of Self-Talk section.) How could you think about this differently?

3. Positive belief and affirmation. Based on the thoughts you identified, write down the core belief that is beneath them, or write down what the voice in your head tells you when it reprimands your behavior.

Then, write down a new statement or belief that is a healthier or positive way of thinking. See the See the Positive Thinking and Affirmations and Uncovering the Lies activities.

4. Action plan. What could you do differently if the situation happened again?

Knowing your tendencies, what could you do to be prepared?

What strengths do you have that will help you?

What can you do if you catch yourself having the same thoughts and behaviors again?

How could you change course?

5. Improvement. After reviewing your experience and thoughts, as well as the alternatives, how do you feel?

Do you feel better, more optimistic, more confident?

How do you think your life will change because you understand your thoughts better?

How will it change if you make these changes?

Additional Journal Prompts

The following are simplified journal prompts that can be used in addition to or instead of the complete ABCDEF Journaling process.

Journal Prompts for Reflecting on the Day

- What went well today? Can you think of five things?
- What was challenging for you today and what did you learn about yourself from that experience?
- What did you enjoy about today? Can you think of particular experience or examples that made you happy during the day?
- What are you grateful for? Can you think of 10 people or things that you have gratitude for today?
- What do you want to feel tomorrow? What do you desire for yourself tomorrow?

Journal Prompts for Reflecting on the Week

- Who made you feel good this week? What did they do or say?
- What was the biggest mistake you made this week? What did you learn about yourself from this mistake?
- How did you surprise yourself this week? Did you do something the old you would have never been able to do?
- What did you do this week that moved you closer to reaching your goals?
- Is there anything you did this week that you wish you'd done differently?
- What did you enjoy doing this week?
- What did you learn this week?

Additional Prompts

- What makes you unique (positive comments only, please)?
- Write your body a letter thanking it for all it does for you (try not to be negative or body-shaming).
- How do you want to be remembered and what do you need to do in order to be remembered this way?
- Make a list of things you want to do before next year.
- Make a list of your best character traits.
- Make a list of your accomplishments, see if you can go through your life span and list 20.
- What are you really good at?
- How would your best friend describe you?
- What would you do if you knew you could not fail?
- Who are your role models and why? How are you on your path to be more like them?
- What would with your time if money were no object?
- If you could become an expert in any subject or activity, what would it be?
- My favorite way to spend a rainy day is…
- What advice would I have for my teenage self?
- The three moments I will never forget in my life are… (Describe them in detail and why they're so unforgettable.)

- What are 30 things that make you smile? (i.e., kitties)
- My favorite words to live by are…
- I couldn't imagine having to live without…
- When I'm in pain of any kind, the most soothing thing I can do for myself is…
- Make a list of the people in your life who support you and whom you trust. (Then make time to hang out with them.)
- How would you define unconditional love?
- How would you treat yourself if you loved yourself unconditionally? In what ways could you act on these things now?
- If others really knew me they would know that…
- What is enough for you?
- If my body could talk, it would say…
- Think about a way you have supported a friend or relative recently. How you can do the same for yourself.
- What do you love the most about life?
- What always brings tears to your eyes?
- What were your first loves in life, such as favorite people, places or things?
- What 10 empowering words best describe you?
- What has surprised you the most, about yourself, related to your ability to thrive in life?
- What lessons have you learned from your biggest mistakes?
- When do you feel the most energized?
- Make a list of everything that inspires you — including people, courses, websites, ideas, art, nature, whatever!
- What's one thing you love to learn more about that would help you live a more fulfilling life? (Great! Now, go study it!)
- When do you feel the most comfortable in your skin?
- Make a list of the things that you've always wanted to say "no" to.
- Make a list of the things you've always wanted to say "yes" to..
- Write yourself a letter telling you what you've always wanted to hear.

Developing Awareness of Thoughts, Emotions, and Behaviors

Cultivating Mindfulness and Self-Awareness

"The outer situation of your life and whatever happens there is the surface of the lake. Sometimes calm, sometimes windy and rough, according to the cycles and seasons. Deep down, however, the lake is always undisturbed. You are the whole lake, not just the surface." – Eckhart Tolle

For most people, the chaos and noise happening around them and within their own minds feels like all there is. They live in a constant state of reactivity, being pushed and pulled by the thoughts and emotions they experience. They're controlled by a voice in their head that worries about everything that can go wrong, criticizes them for everything they do wrong, and feels guilty or angry about everything that went wrong. This voice interprets every situation instantaneously and we don't question it, just like we don't question our breathing. It all happens unconsciously, meaning we are unaware of it. And then we feel and act based on the voice's interpretation.

The truth is that everyone has a voice in their head, including you. Some people's voices are nicer than others, but everyone's voice tends to have the same disfunctions. But the good news—perhaps the best news anyone can ever hear is that this voice is not who you are.

For some of the people reading this course, you already know this well. For others, it may be the first time you have heard it, or the first time you truly understand it. If you've ever argued with yourself over something or you've ever noticed yourself thinking about something ridiculous or you've ever talked to yourself in your own mind, then you've experienced that there are two of you. There is the one that does the thinking, feeling, and reacting and there is the one that is aware of the thoughts, emotions, and reactions. You are that awareness. You are the presence that witnesses the voice, but you are not the voice.

Knowing this allows you to observe what your inner voice is doing and thinking. This is called self-observation or self-awareness. As you become more and more aware of what has always been going on unconsciously, beneath the surface of your awareness, you become conscious. You wake up from the dream. And the process for developing this awareness is called mindfulness.

Until you develop self-awareness and mindfulness, you will likely live much of your life on auto pilot, feeling like you have little control over your thoughts, emotions, or life. The truth is that unless you know what you're thinking, feeling, or doing, you have no way of changing it.

Simply developing this awareness is the key that unlocks all of your power. Power to direct your own inner voice, choose better-feeling emotions, and making better decisions.

Start by listening to the voice in your head as often as you can. Pay particular attention to any thoughts that repeat. Be the observer of what is happening inside of you—both the surface of the lake and the depths. See if you can find and feel the deep calm at the bottom of the lake even when the surface is rough.

As you practice mindfulness and observing your thoughts and reactions, you'll be able to recognize even more clearly that the presence doing the observing is the true you. When you notice yourself feeling angry, you'll observe that the angry part and the part observing it are not the same thing. This is important to know because your true self never becomes disrupted and entangled in these surface level dramas. There is a part of you that is at peace, content, safe, and joyful no matter what is going on around you and in your mind. Your higher self is untouchable, un-disruptable. Knowing it is always there means you can seek to find it in any moment.

And, just like when the sun dips below the horizon you know that it still exists, even though you cannot see it, this calm, peaceful presence that is you is always there, even if you cannot see it.

As you begin to pay attention with a sense of curiosity to discover what your inner voice is up to, you'll begin to notice interesting things it does. You'll notice when you are behaving in a way that is in alignment with our goals and our values, and when you are not. You'll notice when you are smiling even though you are actually sad, or when you say you are fine even though you are not. You may notice you are pretending to be mad when you really aren't, just to manipulate someone else's behavior. Or, you may notice that you are thinking negative thoughts about yourself, making you feel insecure. You may even notice when we are soothing yourself or feeling relaxed or happy.

The last thing you need to know about cultivating mindfulness before we move on is that the doorway to all awareness is the present moment. Most people's minds have a strong habit of spending a lot of time thinking about the past or imagining, and usually worrying about, the future. But the power to observe and redirect your thoughts, emotions, and behaviors is only accessible when you are focused on the present moment. When you're paying attention to what is going on in this moment, you can notice the mind remembering an experience from the past or worrying about the future. But if yourself to go with your mind TO these past or future places, you lose your sense of awareness. For this reason, one excellent way to develop mindfulness and self-awareness is to pay attention as often as you can to what is happening RIGHT NOW. Pay attention to each step you take, to the noises going on around you, to your breathing. Once you pull your awareness back into the present moment, it gives you an opportunity to notice what you're thinking.

It is also important for you to know that the next time you notice yourself experiencing a negative thought or emotion, it doesn't mean you've failed—it means you've succeeded! Until you are able to become aware of these negative experiences you have little power over them. So, every time you notice a negative thought, celebrate! Give yourself a high five! Because now you know that this negative thought is NOT who you are. You are the one in charge and you will be spending the rest of this course learning how to develop this awareness and use proven tools to change the content of your inner world.

Mindfulness Meditation

The term "meditation" often conjures up images of sitting cross-legged on the floor, surrounded by crystals, in a dimly lit room that smells like incense. For some people, this sounds appealing and for others, they assume meditation is a weird, woo-woo, airy fairy experience. But the truth is that meditation is simply a process of observing and quieting your mind. If you don't like the word meditation, call it focusing.

This CBT exercise helps people disengage from obsessive thinking, which means thoughts that have a lot of momentum, by paying attention to the present moment. There has been a significant amount of research conducted on this form of meditation and the positive effects it has on a number of psychological problems.

Simple mindfulness meditation practice:

- Find a quiet place, free of distractions. Your mind will be distracting enough, so make sure you won't be interrupted.
- Sit comfortably in any position you desire. Upright is ideal, however you can lay down if you want to. Just make sure your position is comfortable and will not distract you.
- Start by bringing your attention to your breathing. Notice the sensation of your breath entering and exiting your nose or mouth. Notice how it feels as the air brushes through. Is it cool? Does it tingle?

- Notice the rise and fall of your chest or abdomen as the air fills and then empties your lungs. Do not force or control your breathing, simply allow it to be natural and continue to observe it.
- Watch your breathing for about 5 minutes. During this time, you will find that your mind will wander of and think about all sorts of things: physical sensations, things you need to do, what happened yesterday. This is totally normal. When you notice your mind has wondered off, simply start noticing your breathing again. You may need to bring it back again and again, and this is wonderful because it means you are becoming mindful!
- The more you practice this, the less your mind will wander. Then, you'll notice you are better able to keep your focus at other times throughout the day as well!
- When you are finished with your 5 minutes, you may notice an increased sense of calm.
- As you get used to this activity, you can increase the time sitting to 10, 15, or 20 minutes. What is most important is consistency, so regardless of how long you sit in this mindful state, do it every day.
- The most important part of developing a daily meditation practice is making it consistent. 5 minutes daily is better than 1 hour once a week.

Developing Awareness of Your Thoughts and Self-Talk

There are two layers of thoughts—the ones we can hear or experience as the voice in our head, that makes commentary about ourselves and everything around us, and the deeper level beliefs that determine our opinions, perspectives, and judgments.

CBT primarily focuses on the first category, and specifically on self-talk, which is the part of your inner voice's chatter directed at ourselves. Our self-talk can be an inner cheerleader that motivates and sooths, or it can be an inner critic that is harsh and self-defeating. Our self-talk impacts how we feel about ourselves as well as how we behave and is ultimately responsible for our experience of life and the outcomes that occur because of our actions.

For instance, you may have heard of the concept of a self-fulfilling prophecy, which is a psychological concept that basically means that we will live up to our own expectations or create the situations we expect. For instance, if you are constantly telling yourself you're a failure, it impacts the way you feel—discouraged, self-doubt, anxiety—which impacts how you act and the choices you make. Either you'll make poor choices, like deciding not to try, or when you do take actions, you'll give half-hearted effort. Why bother? You're going to fail anyway, right? In the end, you fail. But it's not because you're a failure, it's because of your thinking.

The deeper level beliefs you hold about yourself, others, the world are what causes your inner voice to talk to you, about you, the way it does. One important thing to know is that you were not born with either a cheerleader voice or a critic voice—you learned how to think this way. How? By observing the way your caretakers and others talked about themselves, about others, and about you. You weren't born fearing failure. When you were a toddler you made a mistake and just kept right on going, that is, until an adult acted like falling down was the end of the world or shamed you for doing something "wrong". Over time, that external voice becomes your internal voice. If you're a parent, think honestly for a second about what you have programmed your child's inner voice to say to them. Ouch, I know.

So, if you just realized that you have programmed some limiting and harsh self-talk into your children, and you're realizing that you've probably been programmed this way too, there is good news: WE CAN ALL BE REPROGRAMMED.

By becoming aware of your self-talk, the positive and the negative, you can CHANGE IT. Self-talk is simply a habit of thinking. So, start out by considering the general predisposition of your inner voice. What percentage of the time do you think your inner voice falls into these 3 categories:

1. Criticize yourself, put yourself down, talk negatively to yourself
2. Make excuses, blame others, tell yourself it's not your fault
3. Tell yourself it will be okay, encourage yourself to learn from the situation

There is nothing right or wrong about your answer to this. Everyone has an inner cheerleader and an inner critic, however the vast majority of people have a very dominant inner critic. This negative side of your thinking can present itself in a variety of ways, which we'll get into in a moment. This is like the fixed mindset persona, but in its full form.

Before we move on, I want to make sure that you always remember that your inner critic is NOT you. So, take a moment and give it a name (you can use the same name you created for your fixed mindset persona). We like to call ours "Bob"!

Negative Self-Talk Triggers

There are 4 common and easy-to-spot ways that your inner critic shines it's light of negativity on your world. Try to catch it in the act. When you notice it thinking one of these types of negative thoughts, simply observe it. Don't judge it or criticize it because if you do, it's just the same inner critic voice coming in the back door again. Think about that one—now you have 2 Bobs! Yikes!

1. **Self-Limiting.** When my Bob is trying to limit me, he says things like "it's too hard, I can't do this" or "it's too risky" or "I don't have time". Ultimately, Bob likes making excuses. This is even more common if you lean toward having a fixed mindset, like we discussed already. When you believe your abilities are fixed and you believe failing means you are a failure, the best way to avoid humiliation is to not try at all—which is what excuses are for, aren't they? Your Bob tries to shut down possibilities and solutions before you even get started.
2. **Assumptions.** Bob's believe they're always right and that they're psychic. They like to think they can read other people's minds and assume what they're thinking and feeling. They like to jump to conclusions and make snap judgments. The Fact or Opinion activity is great if your Bob likes to assume things. Look out for your Bob saying things like "everyone will talk about me", I made a fool out of myself", "she doesn't like me". Your inner critic is making up stories that aren't even true. Once you know this, you won't fall for it so easily.
3. **Re-runs.** Most of our self-talk happens on autopilot. Our repetitive, automatic thoughts have been going on for so long we don't even notice them. Chances are your Bob says things all the time that you don't even actually believe, but you let him get away with it because you're so used it. Often these habits of thought become habits of speech, so you may even catch yourself saying these things to others, out loud. So, be on the lookout for 2 things:
    1. Thoughts, especially memories or anticipated events, that tend to replay a scene in your mind over and over again, like a mini-movie on re-run.
    2. Phrases you say to yourself or others repeatedly, especially if they are making a judgement about yourself.

    For example: "I'm always late" or "I'm an idiot" or "here we go again" or "this always happens to me".

4. **Others' Thoughts.** Sometimes your Bob is simply parroting someone else. You will be shocked when you realize how many of the thoughts that go through your mind are NOT your own. It is time to GET OTHER PEOPLE OUT OF YOUR HEAD. Like I already mentioned, your inner dialog has been programmed throughout your life. Your nagging mom now takes up residence in your mind. The good news, is you can kick her out! The key for this one is to look question the thoughts you have about what you "should" or "shouldn't" do. These words are a sign that the belief behind them was planted by someone else. If YOU actually believed it, in most cases you wouldn't be telling yourself you SHOULD do it, you'd just simply do it.
    - Ask yourself, "Who's voice am I hearing?"
    - Do I really believe that I "should" do this? (Hint, if you're feeling a sense of guilt, it's probably not your own, original, belief.)

- If yes, make it a MUST and do it.

- If not—if this is someone else hijacking your mind, tell them to GET OUT and then ask yourself, what do I really believe?

What's Your Inner Critic's Personality

So, you've named your inner critic so you don't take it so personally and you've learned what to look out for in order to get good at noticing your negative thinking. Now, let's look at 4 common personality types that your inner critic may have. Understanding the way your inner critic tends to think will help you identify what you can do to tame it.

The worrier: Points out everything that can go wrong. Stirs up emotions of anxiety and fear by imagining disasters, expecting the worst, and overestimating the odds of something bad happening. It tends to say "what if"? If your Bob is a Worrier, you can tame it by focusing on the activities in this program that will help ease stress and re-assure your Bob, such as meditation, breathing, visualization, and exposure techniques.

The critic: Constantly judges and evaluates your behavior and points out your flaws. Jumps on any mistake you make and reminds you of past failures. Compares you to others and assumes they will judge you. It even minimizes your accomplishments! It tends to say "you're an idiot". If your Bob is a Critic, you can tame it by focusing on the activities in this program that will help you retrain your thought patterns, such as cognitive distortions, Socratic questioning, and the growth mindset.

The victim: It tells you that you're hopeless, not making progress, or that it's too hard. It tells you there is something wrong with you, your incapable, unworthy. You're not smart enough. There are too many obstacles in your way. It's not your fault. It tends to say "I can't". If your Bob is a Victim, you can tame it by focusing on the activities in this program that will help you take your power back, such as the growth mindset section.

The perfectionist: It pushes you to do better but even when you do better you still feel like you're not good enough. There is always more you should be doing. Mistakes and setbacks must be avoided or quickly moved past. It pushes you to seek external validation, achievement, status. Acceptance by others is of the utmost importance. It probably even stops you from taking action because you're afraid to fail. Tends to say "I need to do better" or "I'm not good enough". If your Bob is a Perfectionist, you can tame it by focusing on the activities in this program that will help you judge yourself less, such as the growth mindset section, overcoming indecision, and overcoming inaction.

Take Your Power Back from Bob

Now that you know what to look out for so you can notice your inner critic in action, go out into the world and practice observing it. When you catch your Bob in the act, use the following 3 strategies to take your power back from these negative thoughts.

3. **Ignore Bob:** Don't take Bob seriously. When Bob starts rambling on incessantly or hops on a negative train, imagine Bob has a funny voice or is wearing a clown suit. Bob is not you, and it doesn't know what it's talking about.
4. **Protect Bob:** Bob's easily influenced, so always ask yourself if YOU really believe what it's saying. We already talked about getting people out of your head. One way to do this is

pay special attention for any thoughts coming from Bob that sound eerily similar to things other people say (such as your parents, the media, authority figures). Choose what you expose Bob to wisely, because he's apt to believe it and repeat it.

5. **Observe Bob:** As often as you can, remind yourself to watch your Bob. Notice what it's thinking about. If you don't like what it's thinking about, CHOOSE A NEW THOUGHT. You're in charge. Many of the activities discussed throughout this course are designed to help you observe, record, and re-direct your Bob.

Remember that it takes time to get good at keeping your Bob in check. You'll notice times when Bob runs off on a tangent of terrible thoughts without you noticing—sneaky Bob! But no worries because when you eventually notice what Bob is doing you can WHACK Bob on the head—it's like playing Whack-a-Mole. Whack him and say "bad Bob!" and laugh. This stops the negative thought, giving you a moment to remember that you have a choice. You can then implement one of the thought-changing strategies you learn in the course and pick a better thought. The more you observe your Bob the better you'll get at catching it in the act—and as you practice, the voice will get quieter and your inner cheerleader will take the lead.

Developing Awareness of Your Emotions

Sometimes people have a difficult time identifying their emotions and it's usually because of one of the following reasons:

- We were made to think our feelings don't matter
- We were made to fear expressing our emotions
- We were made to feel guilty if our emotions (or desires) were an inconvenience on others
- We were discouraged from feeling or expressing specific emotions

Because of our conditioning, some people stop expressing their emotions and often repress them (hold them in). Other people go a step further and stop allowing themselves to have them. In either case, this can lead to a lessened ability to recognize how they feel.

Even people who did not learn to repress or turn off certain emotions—even if they feel things deeply—they can simply not have ever been taught about their emotions and so they cannot clearly identify them. Their emotions feel overwhelming and out-of-control.

If you want to re-gain your power to direct your own emotional state, you need to be able to:

- Notice you're experiencing an emotional state
- Identify what it is
- Know what to expect
- Know how to influence a new emotional state

Emotional States

Emotional States are actually 2 different things:

1. The STATE is the physiological "feelings" that you experience
2. The EMOTION is the psychological interpretation or "label" you put on the state

We experience complex states made up of chemical and hormone interactions that cause a variety of reactions in the body. Our emotions are the interpretations we make of these experiences—or the labels we give them.

So, based on what we talked about in Thoughts Create Emotions, we need to add a couple steps to the process.

Situation → Interpretation (thought) → State → Interpretation (label) → Emotion

What this means is the body responds to the thought first, then our minds interpret the reaction, label it, and an emotion is born. We can have physiological feelings that aren't emotions. We can feel hot, cold, nauseous, or energetic. But when we interpret them to have meaning, we turn them into emotions. Emotions literally mean action: e-MOTION. Each emotional state is designed to get us to do something, and often we do. Our emotional state affects our behavior, but it does not cause it. When we're angry we're more likely to be aggressive, but our cognitive (thought) processes allow us to make those decisions.

The Map is Not the Territory

The labels we give emotions are like a box or a map. What's printed on the box may signal what's inside, but it is NOT what is inside. Just like a map may describe a territory, however it is NOT the territory. Maps are simplified, inadequate and ultimately flawed. It would be like eating a menu. In the same way, what we call "anger", the word, is not the experience. Saying you "love" someone hardly does the experience any justice. In fact, all words are simply signposts pointing toward meaning. The word "tree" is not a tree.

So, what IS an emotion if it's not a map? Well, it's not a "thing" either. You see, labeling an experience as an emotion makes it seem like a NOUN. This is why many people believe emotions are things they HAVE or that happen TO them. The truth is that emotions are verbs (emoting is the verb)—they are a PROCESS. Fear is the process of fearing, which is a string of sensations that occur in a pattern. Fear takes many steps from observation or contemplation to processing and interpreting; then to physiological reaction and FEELING, and finally labeling it as fear.

Emotion Identification Chart:

Below are 6 common emotions and descriptions of the emotion, physiological state, and common resulting behaviors. This chart will help you get a general idea of the signs and symptoms of each emotion to make them easier to identify; specifically, easier to identify early. Everyone experiences each emotion somewhat differently and you may not experience all of the characteristics.

LABEL	EMOTION	STATE	BEHAVIOR
Happiness	Intense, positive feelings of well-being, pleasure, contentment, delight, joy, optimism, and gratitude. Affirmative, positive thoughts and mental clarity.	Head held high (posture), wide-eyed, smiling, laughing, relaxation of muscles, open body language.	Pleasant voice, friendly, swinging arms, dancing.
Boredom	Low-intensity, unpleasant feelings of apathy, restlessness, indifference, empty-ness, and frustration. Defeatist thinking or wishing things were different.	Low energy, slumped posture, smirk or frown, low eyes, shallow breathing.	Resting head, fidgeting, staring.
Anxiety	Vague, unpleasant feelings of distress, uneasiness, stress, apprehension, and nervousness. Thoughts of uncertainty and worry, racing thoughts, difficulty concentrating.	Restlessness, sweating, clammy hands, hunched shoulders, swallowing, quickened breath, darting eyes, butterflies in the stomach, nausea.	Pacing, biting lip, fidgeting. Irritability, hypervigilance.
Anger	Intense, uncomfortable feelings of hostility and hurt. Feeling out of control. Thoughts of blame and resentment. Difficulty thinking clearly or rationally.	Muscle tension, headache, tight chest, increased heart rate, increased blood pressure, heavy breathing, clenched fist, furrowed brow, showing teeth, clenched jaw, sweating, trembling, flushed cheeks, large posture.	Loud voice, yelling, cursing, sarcasm, pacing. Sometimes leads to aggression, including hitting a wall, throwing an object, or lashing out at a person.
Sadness/ Depression	Feelings of intense pain and sorrow, guilt, un-worthiness, disappoint-ment, helplessness, gloominess, loss, grief, numbness, meaning-lessness, loss of interest. Defeated thinking and difficulty concentrating and remembering.	Slumped posture and hunched shoulders, long face, slow movements, pouting, body aches, crying, shaking, crossed arms, fatigue, upset stomach, monotone voice.	Curling up into a ball, laying around, withdrawing, irritability.
Fear	Intense feeling of dread, impending doom, or panic due to a perceived danger or threat. Paranoid or worst-case thinking and hyper focused on the object of the fear.	Increased heart rate, increased blood pressure, alert eyes, high eyebrows, corners of cheeks pulled toward ears, clammy, sweating, quickened breath, goose bumps, butterflies in the stomach, shaky voice.	Freezing, fleeing, hiding.

Practicing Emotional Awareness and Identification

Next time you catch yourself experiencing an emotion that is distinct, ask yourself the following questions. Practice this line of questioning often, especially when experiencing unpleasant emotions.

- How do I feel?
- How do I know?
- What do I feel? Sensations?
- Where do I feel it? Locations?
- Where in my body did it begin? Move to?
- How do I recognize when OTHERS experience this emotion?
- Do I notice any of these signs in myself?
- What do I observe in my body language, vocal tone, thoughts, behaviors?

Situational vs. Psychological Fear

Situational Fear

If our bodies didn't have a natural stress response we would be dead. Actually, our ancestors would have died and we never would have been born at all. Our fight-or-flight response was designed to save our cave-dwelling ancestors from an untimely death in the jaws of a saber-toothed predator or other danger. Our bodies increase our heart rate and send a flood of adrenaline and cortisol throughout our bodies, getting oxygen to the brain and energy to the muscles. This "fear response" provides us an instinctive form of self-protection, allowing us to flee dangerous situations or muster the strength to defend ourselves. *This is situational fear—fear that is triggered by an immediate threat in our current situation.*

It's true that instinctual fear is healthy. It keeps us safe. But many people give fear too much merit—they believe that by living in a state of fear they're somehow protecting themselves and their loved ones. But unless you're under immediate threat, fear is completely unnecessary. You don't need fear to avoid danger – just a minimum of intelligence and common sense. For example, the reason you don't put your hand in the fire is not because of fear. It's because you know that you'll get burned. When a child touches a hot stove and gets burned, they learn that fire equals pain. They learn to avoid touching fire. There is no fear involved.

Now, as an adult this person may be in a home that catches fire—and it would be natural for them to become fearful. The resulting fight or flight response would help them quickly and safely exit the burning building. However, if this person, as a child or an adult, develops a "fear of fire"—meaning when they think about fire they become frightened—they are experiencing psychological fear, not real fear.

Psychological fear

Psychological fear is divorced from any concrete and true immediate danger. It is always fear of something that might happen.

The problem is that while you can always cope with the present moment, you cannot cope with something that is only in your imagination. This is the reason many people report that the thing they were afraid of, when they finally actually experienced it, wasn't "as bad as they expected".

Here is an example of how real fear is different than psychological fear and why the latter is harder to deal with. If you were driving and notice out of the corner of your eye that a car is about to hit you, your body responds, and you enter the fear response. The car swerves and danger is diverted. If this has ever happened to you, immediately after the situation you likely noticed your heart was beating in your chest and your breathing was heavy. You may have noticed your palms were clammy or that you felt shaky. But since it's over, your mind says, "it's okay now" and your body begins to calm down. Within a couple minutes you're back to normal.

This is because the chemicals and hormones and heart rate we experience in order to save our lives are supposed to return to normal after our Neanderthal is sitting around the cave fire telling his buddies about his narrow miss. But in the modern world our bodies don't normalize because our stress isn't caused by threat of death. For us, everything looks like a toothed predator! Our stress is constant! Overbearing bosses, tight schedules, nagging children, distant spouses, and empty hearts put many of us in a state of chronic worry, anxiety and stress.

Our habit of worrying puts us on edge. Then, a stressful situation can agitate us further, adding to the tension we already had and causing physiological reactions, such as increased heart rate, high blood pressure. If we continue to focus on the "problem" causing our state of anxiety, it gets worse. We feel out of control. Our body fully enters the state of fight or flight. And, here's the key… because there is no REAL THREAT happening our mind cannot say "here is the danger and this is what you can do to protect yourself." And because it's not real, your mind cannot stop it and then say "it's over, I'm okay now." The mind, who is trying to protect you, then looks at this fear response and thinks "there must be something wrong." It escalates the situation and you begin to panic. You think there's something wrong with you. You may even think you're dying. You're under attack, but the assailant is YOU.

This is psychological fear, and although the experience is very real, what you are afraid of is imaginary. You are fighting a battle with a phantom shadow.

The best way to win this battle with psychological fear is to stop it before it starts. Remind yourself that it's not real and that you have the power to stop yourself from spiraling into a state of fear. Catch yourself when you're feeling stressed, uncertain or anxious and take action to change your situation, environment or mental focus to help you de-escalate your emotional state.

Identifying Triggers

We all have triggers, both positive and negative. They can be conscious or unconscious. When they are conscious they can be easily identified. More obvious or conscious triggers include: a specific conversation topic, a person, a song, a smell or anything else that we *know* makes us emotional or react a certain way. The biggest challenge we have when addressing our triggers is the fact that most of them are unconscious—meaning we are not aware they are happening.

For example, you may be having a conversation or doing something and you get mad, defensive, or anxious for no apparent reason. You aren't aware of what made you feel that way and so often you blame the person you're talking to or the situation you're in, when the real reason for your reaction is that the situation triggered a learned reaction in your brain. It can be frustrating, however it's important to keep in mind that these triggers were originally created by our brain as a way to help us be efficient with our responses to the world around us and, ultimately, to keep us safe.

Like we talked about in the "You Can Change Your Brain" section, our brain becomes wired when we're exposed to something repeatedly. But another way something becomes strongly wired is when we have an experience that is highly emotional. When we're emotional, our brains assume 2 things:

1. Whatever going on at the time is the cause of the emotion
2. Remembering that this thing is associated with this emotion is important

Once the situation—the place, person, or thing—is programmed into the brain with a certain emotion attached to it, this same thing becomes a trigger, meaning the next time you find yourself with that place, person, or thing, it automatically triggers that same emotion.

The best example is music. If you've ever listened to a song while experiencing emotional situations in your life, that song will forever trigger the emotion to come back when you listen to it in the future. This is why that song you listened and cried when your girl or boyfriend broke up with you still makes your heart ache or why your favorite high school anthem still pumps you up.

Unfortunately, sometimes our brain creates an association between the emotion and a person, place or thing that is NOT truly the cause. When this mis-association happens, the faulty wiring can do more harm than good. For example, if your parents told you "we need to talk" every time just before you got in trouble, then in the future if a friend or spouse says "we need to talk" you'll immediately become defensive. You aren't aware of the real reason you feel that way, and so you blame your friend.

The key to recognizing your negative triggers is to become a student of your own emotions—especially when the emotion does not seem to fit the situation. By becoming aware of triggers, you start to take their power away because you can choose to react differently, instead of reacting automatically.

Ask yourself what tends to trigger emotionally. Then, for each one, consider in what way you react to those triggers and whether the reaction is appropriate or reasonable. Lastly, for each trigger, ask yourself:

- How could I react differently? How could I think differently? Feel differently? Act differently?
- What people trigger me? What do they do or say? What do I think as a response? How do I feel or act? Is it reasonable? What could be different?

- What topics of conversation trigger me? Why? How do I feel or act? What could be different?

- What places do I go that tend to trigger me? What do I think, feel or act? What could be different?

Below are additional common triggers to give you ideas for what to look for:

- ☐ Having to make a change
- ☐ Challenging yourself or learning something new
- ☐ Being criticized
- ☐ Failing at something
- ☐ When something goes wrong
- ☐ When you make a mistake
- ☐ When you make a mistake in front of others
- ☐ Being put on the spot
- ☐ When you procrastinate
- ☐ When you're on a deadline, pressured, or rushed
- ☐ When your reputation is at risk

What other triggers can you think of?

Identifying Underlying Beliefs

Beneath all of your thoughts and behaviors are beliefs that influence you. A belief is just a thought you've thought enough times that you believe it or that was taught to you forcefully enough or that was developed because of an experience you had. Once you believe something to be true, you make assumptions. You make decisions based on what you believe. Your thoughts are directed in the direction of what you believe. But a belief is just a well-habituated thought. The truth is that a very large percentage of what you believe to be true is, in fact, false. But you live out your entire life based on these beliefs. We could do a whole course just on evaluating and changing your beliefs, but learning how to direct your thoughts is the best place to start.

You probably believe that no two finger prints are alike, lightning won't strike the same place twice, dropping a penny from a tall building and hitting someone below will kill someone, cracking your knuckles gives you arthritis and it takes 7 years to digest swallowed chewing gum. But none of these are true. The reason you believe them is you were taught it by people who you thought knew more than you and you just continued to think it. Well, now you know it's all wrong. You're welcome!

But these are just silly, unimportant things you assumed were true… now imagine how many other false beliefs you are carrying around with you! The problem with false beliefs is that they limit you. You make all of your decisions based on what you know, or what you think you know. So if you're wrong, you are potentially missing out on options you didn't know you had. You might be making judgments based on inaccurate information. And these faulty beliefs have real consequences.

Where many coaches, therapists, or people using CBT on themselves make a mistake is they use the techniques to change thinking patterns and redirect emotions in the moment, but they never dig deep enough to uncover the underlying belief that is causing it in the first place.

You might be thinking about how rude and ungrateful your sister is for asking you to babysit AGAIN when you just did two days ago. You're thinking "doesn't she know I have a life? I have things I need to do." You're feeling angry and you're directing it at her. You may be able to change your thinking and focus on the fact that she doesn't normally ask for so much help. This is an exception because everyone in her family has been sick with the flu over the last week and she has things she hasn't been able to take care of. Changing your thinking helps you change your perspective, develop compassion and release your anger. But it doesn't address the underlying belief that was causing you to react that way in the first place.

The underlying belief was probably the belief that if someone asks for your help you are obligated to say yes. The true source of the anger was not at your sister for asking, it was because of your dislike of the feeling of obligation. You were mad at yourself for not knowing how to honor yourself and say no. By identifying and addressing the underlying belief, you can make permanent changes, rather than simply changing the thought and emotion in the moment. You can really look at the belief that you are obligated to help when asked and create a healthier definition for yourself about what it means to be supportive to others, while at the same time honoring yourself. You can develop strategies for setting boundaries, making it easier to say no when you need to AND develop better patterns of thinking about it so that in the future when you agree to help someone, you recognize that it was truly your choice and you do not feel obligated or bitter about it.

To get to the root belief that's beneath your thinking, go through the following questions. You can also combine this activity with other CBT activities to make sure you root out the core of the problem rather than continuing to have to face the same negative beliefs over and over again.

When you identify a negative thought, especially if it is one that you've had over and over again, ask yourself:

- What is the thought I am thinking?

- Who or what is it directed at?

- How do I feel about it?

- Why do I feel that way?

- What do I believe should be different? What rule is it breaking?

- What is the belief?

- What would you have to assume or believe in order to believe this?

- Is there a deeper belief or fear beneath this?

- When is the first time I remember having this thought and feeling this way?

- What experience did I have that caused me to believe this?

- Could you have misinterpreted it? Was there another perspective or other information you may have missed?

- Who do I know that thinks this way or expressed this belief to me?

- What benefits did they receive from believing it or telling you to believe it?

- Are they right? How do you know?

- Keep probing and asking yourself until you get to the core of the belief, then summarize the core, underlying belief.

- On a scale of 1 to 10, 10 being true with 100% certainty, how certain are you that this belief is true? __ How do you know?

- What other possibilities can you think of that might be true instead?

- What would you like to believe instead?

- How does thinking this new belief make you feel?

Thinking back to the original negative thought and the reason behind it, how has how you feel about it changed?

You can dig even further into a process for changing a limiting or false belief and building up a strong new empowering belief to replace it with the Changing Limiting Beliefs activity.

A Note About Acceptance

We have mentioned this throughout the course, but it is worth repeating how important it is to accept your thoughts and emotions as they are.

It is 100% normal to have negative, self-deprecating, limited, or even scary thoughts. Once a thought is focused on long enough, it starts to pull additional, similar thoughts from your memory, as well as see more and more of what you're thinking about around you. This momentum can get you stuck on a train of thinking that can feel like it's going out of control.

At the same time, it is 100% normal to have an emotional reaction to something, especially if it is scary or hurtful. But it is also normal to have a reaction that feels irrational or illogical. Sometimes the programming in our brains causes us to have knee-jerk reactions. It isn't because there is something wrong with us. It is because the brain is trying to protect us.

It's so important to remember that you are normal. It's also important to remember that all emotions and thoughts eventually pass.

The reason this is so important is because if you resist it—if you judge yourself for your thoughts and emotions, if you push against them and add another layer of negative thoughts and emotions on top of it, you only make it worse.

Instead of judging your thoughts or emotions, simply observe them. Notice them. Allow them to be there. Be curious about it, rather than judging. Be gentle with yourself. Then, because you've let go of resistance for a moment, you may find yourself beginning to think more clearly. In that moment, you can remind yourself that you're normal. Everything is okay. This too shall pass.

It's also important to remember that the entire point of learning about all of this is so that you can develop your ability to control it more of the time.

Instead of beating yourself up for your negative thoughts and emotions, celebrate every time you notice that it's happening. Celebrate that although you don't feel in control, you are committed to learning more about your mind and practicing techniques that will help you continue to get better and better at it. You will never be perfect. You'll always have negative thoughts and emotions. But you'll learn how to not take them so personally or seriously. You'll be able to find clarity and peace, even in the most challenging moments. One day you'll be looking back and thinking, "wow, this would have made me freak out in the past, but now I know I have a choice how I react."

You can do this! You just need to be patient with yourself and accept that you were gifted with a wonderful, powerful machine called the human mind. It's quirky and can get it's wires crossed, but now you have the manual and you can continue to reprogram it so that you can use it to reprogram your life.

CBT Technique: Cognitive

Half-Smile Technique

The mind doesn't know the difference between what we're thinking and what is happening in real life, and so it responds by creating an emotional response to our thoughts. The same thing happens with our bodies. When we move our bodies in certain ways, such as smiling, the brain interprets our movements and responds. In this case, when we smile, our brain thinks we must be happy, and so it literally produces happy chemicals. This is called facial feedback. It's so effective, in fact, that call centers have put mirrors up for their operators to seek while they're on the phone, an they're asked to smile at themselves because it has been proven that doing so increases customer service ratings, as well as telemarketing sales.

This simple activity takes advantage of this ability to trick our brains into feeling good and it has been used to treat a number of mood disorders—in fact studies have found it is even more effective than antidepressants!

Here's how it works:

Begin to smile with your lips, but stop just when you start to notice a little tension at the corners of your mouth. If someone was watching you, they probably wouldn't even notice that you're smiling. It's subtle but you can feel it. There is no added benefit smiling really big, and in fact it can make your face get sore during the exercise.

Now, hold your smile for 10 minutes.

You can enhance the benefits by smiling with your eyes too, focusing on the feeling of happiness, or even doing your mindfulness meditation while holding the smile.

The best thing about this exercise is that you can do it anywhere, any time, without anyone noticing, so give it a try the next time you're sitting in traffic or waiting in line.

Square Breathing Technique

As you discovered in the mindfulness meditation section, paying attention to your breathing can help increase focus and decrease stress. This square breathing technique is another method to focus the mind, this time using controlled, deliberate breathing.

Square breathing is very simple. A square has four equal sides. Square breathing has four equal sections. Inhale for 4 seconds, hold it for 4 seconds, exhale for 4 seconds, and then hold for 4 seconds again, and then repeat. If you find it hard to hold your breath for 4 seconds in this cycle, count to 3 when going around your square instead.

It can also be helpful to imagine moving along the edges of a square object, so visualize yourself breathing around the 4 corners of a square, a box, a window, a photo frame, or anything else that's square.

Looking for a simple way to soothe away tension during a stressful work day? Need a break to refocus your attention? Square breathing is a simple, easy, and effective way to calm yourself and enjoy a few minutes of tranquility.

Continue this activity for a minimum of 5 minutes and as you get used to it, expand the amount of time you continue this breathing pattern to 10 or 15 minutes.

Guided Progressive Relaxation

Become aware of your breathing, and notice how your abdomen rises and falls with each breath...

Mentally scan your body for areas of tension. Make note of how your body feels. During this sleep relaxation session, you will focus on releasing any tension in your body, and on quieting the mind. Once the mind is calm and peaceful, you will easily drift into pleasant, restful sleep.

Now take a long slow deep breath in through your nose, all the way down into your stomach. Hold the breath for just a moment, and then exhale through your mouth. Allow your breath to carry away all stress and tension as the air floods out of your lungs.

Imagine what relaxation feels like. It might feel warm...heavy or light...tingly...loose...relaxation is a pleasant, calm feeling...it feels very comfortable.

Take another slow breath in through your nose. Fill your lungs completely. Hold it for a moment...and release the breath through your mouth. Empty your lungs completely.

Take a third deep breath in. Hold it for a moment, and then let it go.

The gentle rise and fall of your chest with each breath is so calming...so relaxing...each time you breathe out...and your chest lowers gently...you feel even more relaxed...

Now let your breathing rhythm return to normal...and relax....

During this relaxation I will ask you to tense various muscles throughout your body. Simply contract each muscle firmly but gently as you breathe in. If you feel uncomfortable at any time, you can simply relax and breathe normally.

Bring your awareness to your feet and toes. Breathe in deeply through your nose, and as you do, gradually curl your toes down and tense the muscles in the soles of your feet. Hold your breath for just a few seconds and notice what that tension feels like. Now, release the muscles in your feet as you breathe out. Feel the tension in your feet wash away as you exhale. Notice how different your feet feel when tensed and when they are relaxed.

Once again, draw in a deep breath...and tighten your calf muscles. Hold for a few seconds, and then let it all go. Feel yourself relaxing more and more deeply with each breath. Your whole body is becoming heavier, softer and more relaxed as each moment passes.

Take another dep breath in… and tense your upper legs. You'll feel the muscles pulling your kneecap upwards. Hold for just a moment, and then release everything. As you do this, the blood flow to your muscles increases, and you may notice a warm tingling sensation. Enjoy this feeling of soothing relaxation.

The Brain Science of Visualization

Professional athletes and performers almost all use visualization because it works. The body does not know the difference between what is happening and what we imagine or remember. When a runner visualizes a race, while attached to electrodes, the exact same sequence of brain activity is observed as when the runner is physically racing.

If you imagine eating a juicy lime and tasting its sour juice, your mouth will salivate because your mind has tricked your body. The same is also true if you visualize yourself failing or losing.

According to research using brain imagery, visualization works because neurons in our brains, those electrically excitable cells that transmit information, interpret imagery as equivalent to a real-life action. When we visualize an act, the brain generates an impulse that tells our neurons to "perform" the movement.

In 2004, the Cleveland Clinic conducted a study on mental exercises and the impact that it has on strength (in participants' fingers and arms). They separated people into three groups and had them follow a protocol for 12 weeks. One group did the physical exercises. One group visualized doing the exercises. The last group did nothing. At the end they re-tested their strength. When it came to finger strength the group that physically did the exercises had a 53% increase in strength, the ones that visualized it had an increase of 35%, and the ones that did nothing had no significant change.

It is incredible to think that your thoughts are so powerful that simply visualizing exercising your finger can significantly increase your strength, without any physical movement.

They also found that arm strength increased by 13% through visualization alone. If your mind can do that, what else can it do for you that you may not be tapping into?

Another study looked at the brain patterns of weightlifters, both when they were lifting hundreds of pounds and when they were only imagining lifting. They found the brains were activated similarly by the actual and imaginary lifting. Many studies have found mental practices are almost as effective as physical practice, with the greatest benefit being combining the two. For example, another study at Cleveland Clinic, conducted by exercise psychologist by Guang Yue, compared "people who went to the gym with people who carried out virtual workouts in their heads". The gym-goers had a 30% increase in muscle strength, while the participants who exercised only mentally increased their strength by 13.5%, which is nearly half the benefit with none of the work! This actual strength from imaginary exercise remained for 3 months following the mental training.

This is important! What we imagine and visualize ourselves experiencing: a) impacts our brain and body and b) creates real outcomes in our lives.

First, think about what you're doing to yourself every time you re-live those old yucky memories and replay them over and over again in your mind? You're right, you actually ARE reliving them! This is why you can continue an argument with your boss or spouse hours after the real one happened, or days before you actually confront them, yet you feel the same rush of angry emotions flood your body. Yup, your body think's it's real. Stop it!

Second, think about how powerful it would be if you used the newfound knowledge about how your mind and emotions work deliberately, in order to create positive emotions through positive imaginings? Imagine if you mentally created the future life you want to live and rehearsed how it would feel, what it would look like, who you would be, and what it would be like to live your dreams NOW in your mind? You can, because your mind doesn't know the difference, remember? Why not go there now?

That's exactly what you're going to do next.

Create a Vision of Your Future

Looking back at everything you've learned about your irrational thinking and the beliefs that were holding you back, we hope that by now you can see that you have more potential than you ever could have imagined! You are the proud owner of the world's most powerful machine, and now you have a better idea of how to use it!

After banishing your limiting beliefs and reigning in your monkey mind, you can envision a future for yourself with more clarity and hope than ever before. Now, you can dream your dreams and feel confident that you have the mindset and tools to make the necessary changes within yourself to get there. Go you!

So, the last exercise in this course is to create a vision of your future! Look back at what you identified that you want in your life in Section 11.7. When writing your vision, use the desires you identified and write your story of your future self as if it's happening now.

With your newfound understanding of where your thoughts, beliefs and desires come from, you will be able to create a vision of your future from a place of genuine desire, not irrational demands and musts. You'll dream your dreams without being limited by "shoulds". When your negative self-talk pops-up, you will know what to do, and you will have the ABCDEF process and other tools from this Human Mind Owner's Manual to give your monkey mind a banana when it needs one!

When writing your vision, follow the same 4 P's rules from the positive thinking and affirmations section:

1. Personal (I, Me statements)
2. Passion (put emotion into it)
3. Present (as if it's already happening, not future or past)
4. Positive (avoid words like "not" or "don't")

Most importantly, write your vision from a growth mindset perspective, knowing that whatever it is you dream to do, you can learn, grow and improve in order to get there.

Reframe Negative Experiences

Imagine each situation in life is like a photo in a frame. The frame that holds the photo influences how the photo appears. Other things around the photo also impact how you perceive it, such as the lighting, the color of the wall, or where it's hung. These differences can even change the meaning of the photo. A photo of an explosion that is hanging on the wall in an office building that says "blow up your limits" means something totally different than that exact same photo hanging on a wall in a war memorial museum. With any photo or situation in life, if you change the frame or the way you're looking at it, the meaning changes.

That's why we change our perspective of a situation, we call it "reframing".

The Power of Interpretation or Perspective

You may not always be able to change what happens around you, but you always have a choice of how you respond, react, and how you view the situation. The situation itself does not determine the outcome, your perspective does.

Even the worst experiences of life, that feel like a curse, can be re-framed to find the blessing contained within them. It is the MEANING we attach to a situation that determines whether it moves us forward or holds us back.

Finding the Silver Lining

For every seemingly negative circumstance in life, there either was (or could be) a positive outcome because of it.

- If your relationship hadn't ended bitterly, you may not have the loving relationship you have today.
- If you had not been downsized during the recession, you may not have returned to school and changed your career.
- If you had never made mistakes, you never would have learned the lessons that made you who you are today.
- If you had never experienced loss of a loved one, you would not have the same appreciation for those in your life today.

The moral of the story is that you always have a CHOICE of to look for the silver lining in any situation.

Reframe Negative Experiences

When something happens that makes you frustrated, sad, angry, or disappointed, ask yourself the following questions:

- What else might be going on here?
- What did I learn from this experience?
- What can I do differently next time?
- What positive outcome eventually came as a result of this situation?
- What meaning does it have? What purpose does it give me?
- How can I use this for GOOD?

Practice: On the following page, make a list of any experiences from your past that were "negative" and then identify the positive outcomes and/or the empowering lessons you can take from them.

“Negative” Experiences	Positive Outcomes

Change Your Perspective and Your Words

The words you use are one powerful way to shift your perspective. For example, the word "fail" can conjure up strong emotions and fear. To someone with a fixed mindset, failure is the ultimate worst-case scenario because it means you ARE a failure.

By changing your perspective, you can change the way you view failure. Let's try it now.

The truth about failure is that as long as you learn something from it that you apply to your life, nothing is lost. It is only failure if you either don't learn from it and give up or if never try in the first place.

Imagine you wanted to climb a mountain. You're standing at the bottom looking up, feeling afraid that you might fail. But you are already in the failure position. Why? Well, because if you tried climbing the mountain and failed, you'd end up back where you are. So, not trying to climb the mountain is the same as failing.

There are also many stories of famous failures that illustrate how failure is not a death sentence. Walt Disney was fired from a job and was told he lacked imagination. Steven Spielberg was rejected by the cinematic school he applied to. But they didn't see their failure as a reflection on themselves, they saw their failure as a learning opportunity.

Using the analogy of the mountain to see that not trying is the same as failure takes the fear out of failure because you realize you have nothing to lose. Finding evidence that supports that failure is not a bad thing helps us remember to look for the silver linings and what can be learned.

Another step you can take is to change the words you use. For instance, next time you hear yourself thinking or saying the world "fail", replace it with "learn". The new word helps you re-frame the situation and remember to look for the lesson.

Here's another example: the next time you catch yourself thinking "I'm not good at this", always add the word "yet". This lets your mind know that although you may not have the ability, this does not mean you can't. By telling your unconscious mind that you can develop the ability, you have given it a command and it immediately starts to tune into finding ways for you to learn and grow. This is the power of your words to change your perspective.

What words do you tend to use to talk about failure, your weaknesses, or to put yourself down?

What words could you use instead?

Positive Thinking and Affirmations

Positive Thinking

When you're in the midst of having a negative thought and the associated negative emotion it can be really hard to think positively. Even if the negative thought is faulty or untrue, it feels so right and real in the moment.

Positive thinking isn't about fooling yourself, it's about thinking MORE positively than your current negative state. That's why it's important to practice improving your thoughts, gradually. You see, the thought has momentum, like a car rolling down a hill. If you try to jump out in front of it and force yourself to change your thought, it will run you right over.

If you're thoughts are telling you "I'm unworthy", trying to tell yourself "I am powerful and amazing" may sound ridiculous to yourself at the time. It's unbelievable. Instead, you need to slow it down with incrementally better thoughts. Instead of reaching for the best thought ever, just try to reach for something a little better that feels believable to you from where you are. For instance, start with "I matter to a few people" and then "I have done important things in the past" and work your way up to "what I do with my makes a difference to others" and finally to "I matter".

Another way to counteract negative thoughts is to be preemptive. Instead of waiting until you're in the midst of a powerful negative thought to try to change your mind, practice positive thoughts ahead of time. Doing this can reprogram your thoughts and prevent those negative thoughts from happening, and when they do they are less powerful.

This process, often called affirmations, is the most effective when used for negative thoughts that you have regularly.

Affirmations

Affirmations are written or spoken positive statements that, when consistently practiced, rewire our thoughts and beliefs.

If you have a repetitive negative thought that causes you to feel bad, you can replace it with an empowering thought. If you repeat it to yourself regularly, such as when the negative belief is triggered AND at pre-determined times of the day, you practice this new belief, helping it become ingrained into your implicit, automatic, memory. Over time this thought becomes habituated and you BELIEVE it.

After you have created your affirmations, the next time you catch yourself thinking one of those repetitive negative thoughts, you can remind yourself of the new positive thought you've created to replace it. Because it's something you do repeatedly, using this new thought helps slow the momentum of the negative thought much faster than the first method we discussed.

The 4 P's for Successful Affirmation Statements:

1. Personal (I, Me statements)
2. Passion (put emotion into it)
3. Present (as if it's already happening, not future)
4. Positive (avoid words like "not" or "don't")

Lastly, you must repeat it REGULARLY.

Affirmation Activity:

For this activity you can focus on one thought you are looking to counteract, or you can brainstorm a number of different repetitive thoughts. What NEGATIVE BELIEFS to you commonly think to yourself (or even say out loud) about yourself, your capabilities, your confidence, or anything else that holds you back?

For each negative belief, write a NEW phrase that is positive and empowering, using the guidelines above. Ask yourself, what would counteract the negative thought—nullify it? What would be the opposite? What do you WANT to think or believe in this situation?

Common Negative Belief	New, Positive Belief

Repeat this affirmative statement at least 3 times a day (5 to 10 times each session). Consider posting it on your mirror, computer or nightstand where you can see it regularly.

The next activity uses a similar process to identify the lies we tell ourselves or the negative thoughts we think about ourselves and replace them with the truth!

Uncovering the Lies

When you are completing this activity, focus on one category at a time.
Materials you'll need:

- 1 pen
- 1 pencil
- 10 sheets of lined paper (as many as you need)

How to Uncover the Lies and Rewrite Them

Step 1: Identify the Lies

- Start with your **pencil**. Write down a lie your inner critic tells you about yourself.
- Skip 4 lines
- Staying in the same life category, write down another lie.
- Skip 4 lines
- Once you've exhausted beliefs in this category, move onto another category and repeat.

For example:
I'll never get married.

Step 2: Tell the Truth

- Put away your pencil and take out your pen.
- On the line under each lie, you're going to write the truth. The truth could be the opposite of your lie or it could be simply something nicer. Reach for the highest level, self-affirming belief you can find. *NOTE: Make sure your truth is written as a positive statement. Do not use "not" or "no" or "isn't" or "don't". For example, if your lie was "I am stupid" your truth would not be "I am NOT stupid" it would be "I am intelligent at many things".*

Step 3: 7 Daily Reminders

Next, read the lies and the truths to yourself every day for 7 days.
On the 7th day, ERASE the lies.
Revisit this activity any time you need a pick-me up, a reminder, or if you discover there are more limiting, critical beliefs you want to uncover and replace.
Activity sheet on the following page.

Lie (write in pencil):
Truth (write in pen):
Lie (write in pencil):
Truth (write in pen):
Lie (write in pencil):
Truth (write in pen):
Lie (write in pencil):
Truth (write in pen):
Lie (write in pencil):
Truth (write in pen):
Lie (write in pencil):
Truth (write in pen):

Changing Limiting Beliefs

The Table Leg Method

Imagine your belief is like a tabletop and the evidence that supports your belief is like the table legs. You look at the evidence and make a conclusion—a belief about it. Just like with a table, if you knock enough legs out from under it the belief will collapse. You do this by creating doubt about your evidence or looking at it in a different way. Then, after you collapse the old, unwanted belief that makes you doubt yourself or your dream, you can use the same method to build up a new one. That's right, it works in reverse! If you determine a belief that is more empowering that you'd prefer, you can find evidence that SUPPORTS your new belief. Add at least 3 legs and the table will stand.

For example, if you believe that you are bad at math, you may have several reasons for this belief. First, it seems to run in your family. In fact, your mother said it's in her genes. This plants the first seed. Then, in 5th grade you got a math answer wrong when you were asked to do the math problem on the board in front of the class. It was embarrassing and reinforced your belief, making you thing "geeze, I guess mom was right!". Then, you failed the last two tests you took in your high school algebra class. You felt bad about it. Now the belief is stuck.

But believing that you are innately bad at math will hold you back. First, because you expect to do poorly you'll be more nervous when you take math tests, you'll be less likely to try harder or practice since you believe you're simply unable to do math. You will unintentionally prove yourself correct. This is called a self-fulfilling prophecy. In the end, you'll avoid things that you might have enjoyed simply because you expect they'll involve math and you don't want to do it because you think you're bad at it. Maybe you love science, but you never pursued a career in science because you didn't think you could do the math. Maybe you wanted to start a business but didn't think you could handle the finances because of your math deficiency.

When we hold limiting beliefs, they hold us back from our potential.

The good news is even the more strongly held beliefs that hold up the overall belief can be undone. The key is to question the evidence we use to support it, remove the superglue, and find a new, more empowering belief to replace it with.

Before we begin, it's important to understand that when we're talking about limiting beliefs, we are not saying that the belief is FALSE. It may be true or based on things that really happened. But whether it's true or false isn't the point. We're looking at beliefs that are either empowering or disempowering. They're either useful or harmful.

5 Step Process for Changing Limiting Beliefs

STEP 1: Identify a limiting belief you would like to change: Make a list of all of the things you can think of that provide evidence (table legs) that support your belief (at least 3 pieces of evidence).

STEP 2: Identify an alternative belief that is more empowering: If you're having a hard time identifying a more empowering belief, ask yourself "what if I believed the opposite"? You want to choose a new belief that is believable. So, instead look for an IMPROVED belief. So, that could be "there is always opportunity in the market if you provide an exceptional product or service."

STEP 3: Unstick the emotional superglue: Sometimes we become emotionally attached to our limiting beliefs. We experience benefits or emotional payoffs for keeping our limitations around, which makes them sticky. It is like supergluing the table legs to the floor.

What is the emotional payoff for holding onto this belief? Be honest with yourself. Write down everything you can think of that may be an emotional or practical benefit.

Step 3: Emotional Payoffs/Evidence	Step 4: Create Doubt

Next, ask yourself: do these benefits outweigh the costs of keeping this limitation? __Yes __No

- If your answer is YES—that the emotional payoff is worth it—then you will most likely NOT be able to change this belief because you are too attached to it.
- If you answer is NO—the payoff is NOT worth continuing to be limited by this belief—well, then it's time to celebrate because you've just dissolved the superglue! You actually WANT to change, and that means it's time to start dismantling that table.

STEP 4: Create doubt by reframing your evidence:

Like we said, you believe what you believe because you look at the evidence and come to a conclusion. But what if the evidence was wrong, incomplete, or you just weren't seeing it clearly? That would make you question your conclusion, and that's exactly the point of this step. For **each piece of evidence (emotional payoffs above)** you identified for your limiting belief, ask yourself the following questions (in the box above):

Could this be untrue?

Is there more to the story?

What is an alternative explanation?

The point is to question the evidence enough to create doubt. Some evidence will be harder to refute than others, but that's okay as long as you can knock out enough to leave less than 3 legs standing!

STEP 5: Find evidence to support your new belief:

Now we're gong to flip this around and build up the supporting evidence to solidify your new belief. Looking back at your desired belief, make a list of everything you can think of that supports this new belief. You only need a minimum of 3 but you want to create as many legs as possible so that this belief is way stronger than the old, limiting one.

What supporting evidence is there to support your new, desired belief?

With enough supporting legs, your new belief will stand. It might not be as strong as your old belief at first, but that is okay.

In many cases, the table legs that held up your old belief may have been really thick or really superglued because of the emotions tied to them. When thinking about evidence for your new belief, it may be harder to find emotionally-charged evidence, so you want to think of as many things as you can. The number of supporting legs will make up for the less powerful examples.

Behavioral Experimentation

Step 1: Identify the Behavior that You Wish to Change
This can be a habit or pattern you want to stop, a decision you want to make, an emotional pattern you want to change, a limiting belief that's holding you back.

Step 2: Explore the "What if's"
Behavioral experiments help you find out the answer to the question "What if?"

Explore the "What if's"	The practical potential outcomes	Your expected behavior	How you feel about each possibility
What if I chose a different option?			
What if I did this another way?			
What if I approached this differently?			
What if I looked at this from a different perspective?			

What if I did the opposite?			
What if what I am assuming is wrong?			

The second step is to test them in real life. Ask yourself:

- Of everything I experimented with mentally, which ways of thinking or options do I want to explore further?

- Which ones seem most likely to have the desired impact on my behavior and outcomes?

- For each, what can I do to test this?

Overcoming Indecision Part 1: Autopilot and Being Stuck

Indecision is a form of self-abuse. It's the ultimate form of giving away your power because it is our decisions that determine our destiny. One of the most important aspects of life that CBT can help with is decision making.

The first form of indecision is being on autopilot.

Some people don't make decisions at all. In fact, they aren't even aware of what they're doing. They blindly follow their impulses, or worse, their familial and cultural assumptions of how life "should" be. Many people respond to the stimulus of their environment with knee-jerk reactions, and their lives unfold on autopilot.

In the most extreme situations, their choices dramatically reduce their options, like choosing to drive recklessly and ending up in an accident that causes permanent disability or accidentally becoming pregnant at 15. Other decisions are more subtle, yet have lasting repercussions. Some people choose to settle for a practical career that they hate or take over the family business out of obligation. They may go to college for a degree they don't want or drop out because they don't know what they want. They may get married, have children, and climb the corporate ladder because it's what they're "supposed" to do. They may fall into habits or patterns that don't serve them or keep experiencing the same dysfunctional relationships over and over again. They may spend hours a day on social media or watching TV instead of working toward their dreams. They never stop to question their decisions and, if they do, it's often only after they're already suffering the consequences. They aren't aware that they could have had a totally different and, most likely, dramatically more epic life.

If you've been living your life on autopilot, this entire course is designed to help you become more aware of your thoughts and behaviors, which means you will be more conscious of the decisions you are, and are not, making. If you've been giving away your power, the exciting thing is now you know that you can take it back. Get in the habit of asking yourself what you want, as well as taking a moment to consider the outcomes or repercussions of the actions you take.

The second form of indecision is being stuck.

This happens when you recognize that you have a choice how to live, but you either cannot decide between your options or you cannot get yourself to move forward. You're stuck. There are 4 ways you can get stuck.

1. **Not Sure What You Want:** There may be times you don't take action because you're not sure what you want and so you do nothing. Like so many people, you might reach a decision point and then think and think and think, but never act. But you are still making a decision because your indecision will ultimately lead to an undesirable outcome. By not deciding, you give away your power. Often, indecision means you wait too long and your choices are no longer available. Other times, it means you allow someone else to make the choice for you. The saddest form of indecision is when you know what you wanted but you let it slip away. See the Fear Setting activity.
2. **Perfectionism:** One of the things that gets in the way for many people is perfectionism. Don't worry whether it's the "perfect" decision or whether it's the "right" direction. Making *any* decision in *any* direction gets things moving. For example, if you got in your car, turned on the GPS, and told it where you wanted to go, it may not initially lead you to the right direction if it does not recognize which way you are facing or if has not updated your location. However, as soon as your car starts moving it will get oriented and then tell you to go in the direction you need to go, even if it means turning around. The same thing happens when you take action in life. Getting started is the hardest part, but once you make a move—any move—it becomes easier to assess if you're

going the right way and what steps to take to correct your path. See the next section where we'll talk about creating the spark to take that first step.

3. **Being Indecisive:** Are you not sure which option to choose?

   Try each one out. Taking even one step in one direction or another will help you gauge how you feel about it. If it is not possible to literally take a step or try it out, run through the possibilities in your mind. Imagine making the decision one direction. Imagine taking the first step.

   - From there, what are the possible outcomes?
   - How do I feel about each outcome?
   - For each outcome, what are the possible next steps?
   - Then, make the next decision and ask again…

See the Exposure Techniques activity for a process that will help you use visualization to try out different options.

4. **Feeling Uncertain:** Are you avoiding making a decision to move forward on something because you're not sure how it will turn out? Uncertainty is a big roadblock for many people. It's normal to wish you could know how everything will turn out ahead of time, but the problem is that you can't. The solution is to take a small step. Test the waters. And in many cases, just simply do it! If you can't get yourself to make the leap, work through the steps of the process in your mind and check out the next section about overcoming inaction.

Overcoming Indecision Part 2: Irrevocable Choices

Becoming aware of the thought processes that are keeping us from making a clear-minded decision, as well as getting clear about what we want, can help us make better decisions.

But the truth is that some decisions are harder than others. Use the activity below to help you weigh those more difficult options.

The third form of indecision happens when the choices are irrevocable, meaning the repercussions of either choice are life changing. Sometimes we're faced with the terrifying reality that when we choose one path it means we will permanently eliminate our other options.

This is why so many people never make a leap into the unknown. They are paralyzed by fear—fear that they'll make the wrong decision. Fear they'll regret what they'll miss out on. They spend so long standing in trepidation that eventually they find themselves living the default life that their environment cultivates. The only difference between them and those who live on autopilot is that they ache inside for the dreams they never chose because they were aware of their options. But it's too late—the ship has sailed. What they didn't realize is that whether they made that hard decision or not, a decision was made and something was lost. It's inescapable.

Some people run from the truth and avoid pain so much that they miss out on life completely.

When faced with such earth-shaking dilemmas, how do you choose?

How do you choose whether or not to leave a marriage? How do you decide to quit your job and go back to school? How do you decide whether the freedom of entrepreneurship is worth the risk and uncertainty? How do you decide to move thousands of miles from your family and friends and miss out on important milestones? How do you decide whether or not to have a child?

All five of those life decisions are ones that I have made. Each one tore me open inside. Some life-changing decisions are easier than others.

I have found—through intensive firsthand experience, research into success and happiness, and experiences with my clients—that there are 2 stages we must go through to make those really hard decisions:

1. Honesty
2. Acceptance

1) HONESTY: We must be honest with ourselves about what we will lose, on both sides of our decision.

I like to think about it like this. No matter what choices we make in life, we are destined to have a ghost ship— that contains all of the experiences, people, and options we did not choose. This ship is like an alternative version of our life that lives on without us, floating adrift in an infinite sea. I find this idea to be a great relief. We never have to let something go entirely because part of us holds it in our hearts forever.

The question, then, which of our options do we let sail away?

The following activity will help you really look at the benefits and consequences of each option.

Consider the decision you face, and imagine you are choosing to live LIFE #1 and allowing LIFE #2 to drift out to sea.

1. What are the positive, meaningful **outcomes** I'll experience if I choose LIFE #1?

2. What are the negative, meaningful **losses** I'll experience because I did NOT choose LIFE #2?

Now, switch your choice around in your mind, allowing LIFE #1 to drift to sea, and imagine what it would be like.

1. What are the positive, meaningful **outcomes** I'll experience if I choose LIFE #2?

2. What are the negative, meaningful **losses** I'll experience because I do NOT choose LIFE #1?

Put it all on paper. Include everything you can think. Be brutally honest.

And when you're ready, really ready to know your answer, sit down and ask the final question. When you're 85 years old, which one would you regret NOT doing more?

At the end of this exercise, you'll be clear. Devastatingly clear. But that's okay because the weight will be lifted; the decision will be made. And, most importantly, you won't risk letting life pass you by, robbing you of your potential for greatness.

2) ACCEPTANCE: Next, you must accept the life that is truly yours to live and honor the one you are leaving behind.

You may never know what it was like to live the life you don't choose. It wasn't yours to live. But you'll be able to live the destiny you have created, knowing you made an empowered decision that honored who you truly are. Some of what you've left behind will fade from your mind completely; some will echo in your heart forever.

In order to create my beautiful life, I have sent many possibilities, people and pieces of myself to live upon my ghost ship.

When I find myself facing another irrevocable choice, I am drawn to the sea. I stand on the shore with the waves lapping my feet. When I look to the horizon, I catch a glimpse of what looks like the shadow of a sail. I wiped away a tear, smile and waved gently to my phantom self and my life that I'll never know, knowing that no matter what I choose, part of me will always be adrift.

Bon voyage.

Overcoming Inaction

Do you ever find yourself knowing what you need to do but just not able to get yourself to do it?

In order to understand why this happens, you need to understand activation energy. In chemistry, activation energy is the term used to describe the phenomenon that a tremendous amount of energy is needed in order to start any chemical reaction. Then, after this initial spark, a lot less energy is needed to keep it going.

Activation energy applies to human behavior too. Not having activation energy is why it can be so hard to get started, whether we're trying to go to the gym, make a phone call, or get out of bed.

Sometimes we need to create a SPARK to get us moving, that's big enough to keep us going. Other times we need to light a fire under our butt to remind us the big reason why we need to take this action.

So, the best strategy to create the SPARK that helps you take the first step toward ANYTHING is to use the 5-second rule. *(We have author and speaker Mel Robbins to thank for this gem!)*

Why 5 seconds? Because your brain is wired to avoid risk and fear change. When the thought comes to your mind of the thing you want to do (but that you haven't done because of fear or resistance), if you wait more than 5 seconds your brain will try to talk you out of it, again. It will bring up all of the reasons you "shouldn't" do it, why it isn't a good time, what could go wrong, or the most clever one—"I don't feel like it." Well, unless what you're trying to do is 100% pleasurable (which it can't be, otherwise you wouldn't have to make yourself do it) chances are you will NEVER "feel like it". Now, don't get me wrong, I'm not suggesting you should be forcing yourself to do things that truly aren't right for you. Don't make yourself suffer. Don't go against what your heart is telling you. But if your heart is telling you YES and your body still won't get in gear, give it a nudge!

By taking action, any small action, within 5 seconds you outsmart your own brain.

Here's how the 5 SECOND RULE works:

Anytime you have an idea that will better your situation, act IMMEDIATELY—within 5 seconds. Don't think, just do!

When the thought comes, start counting from 5 down to 1 and GET MOVING. There are 2 reasons that THIS IS THE KEY TO WHY THE 5 SECOND RULE WORKS!

1. It signals to your brain that there is an END to the countdown. If you counted from 1 to 5 you could keep going.
2. Counting distracts your mind, preventing it from thinking you out of it.

So, next time an idea comes to mind of something you know that if you did it you'd receive positive results, use the 5 second rule to DO IT NOW. When the thought comes, "I should make that phone call" count 5… 4… think of where your phone is… 3… 2… reach for your phone… 1… dial the number.

There are so many uses for this! Before I had ever heard of the idea of the 5 second rule, I used this immediate action strategy on MYSELF to get myself to stop procrastinating doing the dishes.

Then, when it worked, I used it on everything! I'd notice my resistance and use that as a trigger to act IMMEDIATELY.

Another excellent use of the 5 second rule is to start a new habit! Breaking an old habit requires you to replace it with a new habit. You can use the 5 second countdown to start the new ritual that will interrupt the old behavior pattern.

Scheduling Activities

Action Step	When I Will Do It	What I Need	Goal/Outcome

Don't Forget to Plan in the Fun!

First, identify fun or pleasant activities that you would like to do.
Aim for activities that will take you less than ten minutes.

- What do you enjoy doing already that you want to do more of?
- What activities feed you, lift your spirit, or make you feel energized that you love but that you don't do now?

Then, schedule them in!

- Pick a day every week to plan in the fun.
- Schedule one pleasant (and healthy) activity every day that you normally wouldn't do.
- Schedule an activity every day that gives you a sense of mastery, competence, or accomplishment. Again, choose something small that you wouldn't usually do.
- An advanced version of this technique would be to schedule three pleasant activities per day in the morning, afternoon, and evening.

Exposure Techniques for Overcoming Fear and Resistance

Often the best way to overcome anything that you resist or are afraid of is to expose yourself to it in a way that gently gets you used to it. You can accomplish this gradual desensitization effect both mentally and in real life.

Play the Script Until the End (the Worst-Case Scenario)

Another great process for overcoming fear and resistance is to actually face the fear itself. The way you do this is to imagine the situation and play the script all the way to the end, which would be the worst case scenario that you are afraid of. The benefit of doing this is that you can see what it would actually be like without having to experience it in real life. It gives you a safe place to see how it would feel and determine how you would cope with it. See the De-Catastrophizing and Fear Setting activities.

Imagery Based Exposure

The mind does not know the difference between reality and what is happening in the mind. Whether a situation is happening or you're imagining or remembering it, the brain reacts the same by producing the neurochemicals that make you feel an emotional response. This means that if you are afraid of something, whether it's public speaking, bringing up a difficult conversation, or riding in an airplane, you can use visualization to practice exposure mentally. This tool can also be used to practice a new skill or make a life change. Change can be scary, so using visualization is one way to overcome resistance by getting used to the experience ahead of time. You can work through the intimidating parts in your mind and play out all of the different options so that you know ahead of time how you want to react when it comes time for the real experience. Skills can also be practiced using visualization because imagining executing the skill or steps in great detail helps the brain create a habit of thought. Then, when you take the steps in real-life, it doesn't feel new, it feels like you've done this before.

Regardless of the situation you wish to expose yourself to mentally, determine what the experience would look like. Would there be steps to take? What would be going on around you? Who would be there? Sit down, close your eyes, and imagine the experience from start to finish. Imagine every step in great detail. When you experience a negative emotion of resistance or fear, observe how it feels. Ask what you are thinking about the situation that is making you feel that way. Ask yourself what you would want the experience to look like in order for you to feel more comfortable with it. Then, continue imagining the experience going well. Imagine yourself feeling comfortable and content. You can even add fun or relaxing elements to the scene if you want, such as music or color. Imagining the situation with these added elements helps program the mind to expect to feel good when the situation happens in real life. You may need to do this activity several times until you can go through the entire process feeling good.

How could you use this technique?

Situation Exposure Hierarchies

Another way to gradually expose yourself to something in a way that overcomes resistance and fear is to take baby steps. First, identify something, or multiple things, you are avoiding. Then, identify what steps or actions involved in this situation that you are feeling resistant to doing. This could be having a conversation, committing to something, taking an action, making an investment, etc. For each of the aspects that you feel resistance about, rate them on a scale of 1 to 10, 10 being extremely high resistance or fear. Put the different aspects or steps in order based on their score. Then, start taking the steps with the lowest level of resistance first, working your way up to the more difficult steps. Doing this builds confidence, and because the smaller tasks are already out of the way, you will feel less overwhelmed and will build your way to the more difficult steps.

How could you use this technique?

Fact or Opinion

Thoughts are not facts. Most people assume that thoughts are equivalent to facts, but that is rarely true! It takes practice to learn how to identify the difference between opinion and fact. In the activity below, next to each statement decide whether it is a fact or an opinion.

When you catch yourself making a judgment, check in to identify if you know your thought is an actual fact or if it is an opinion or guess.

	FACT:	OPINION:
• 1. "She is a bad person" • 2. "Amanda told me she didn't like what I said in the meeting" • 3. "Nothing ever goes my way" • 4. "This project is going to be a disaster" • 5. "I'm not as good looking as he is" • 6. "I failed the test" • 7. "I am overweight" • 8. "She yelled at me" • 9. "He is selfish" • 10. "There's something wrong with me" • 11. "I'm lazy" • 12. "My friend didn't lend me money when I asked" • 14. "My feet are too big" • 15. "I'm ugly" • 16. "Nobody will ever love me"		

Answers: Facts (2, 6, 7, 8, 12), Opinions (1, 3, 4, 5, 9, 10, 11, 14, 15, 16)

What judgments are you making?

JUDGMENT:	FACT:	OPINION:

Putting Thoughts on Trial

Pretend as if you are putting your thoughts on trail. You are trying to prove it WRONG. You will you play the defense attorney, the prosecutor and the judge. You will provide evidence for and against the thought, in order to determine if it is based on fact,

Write down the thought that you want to put on trial.

- The Defender: What evidence will you present to the Judge to support it?

- The Prosecutor: What evidence will you present that calls the other evidence into question?

- The Judge: Now that you've seen the evidence from both sides, as an impartial judge, how would you rule in this case?

Alternative Action Formula

Problems and Difficulties
List all of the problems you are currently having

Vulnerabilities
What makes you more likely to experience this problem than someone else?

Triggers
What made these problems so bad right now?

Coping Strategies	**Effects of These Coping Strategies**	**Alternative Actions**
What do you do to cope with these problems?	How do these strategies make you feel in the short term?	If your current solutions aren't completely effective, what else could you try?
	Long term?	
What makes you feel better, at least temporarily?		
	What are the advantages and disadvantages?	

Functional Analysis

Antecedents (factors that preceded a behavior)	Behaviors	Consequences (what happened as a result of the behavior?)
Consider situational (where, when), social (who was/wasn't there), and emotional states.		*What are the short/long term factors that make this behavior more likely to happen again?*

Modifying Rules and Assumptions

What is the rule (or assumption) I live by that I would like to modify?

How does this rule (or assumption) affect me in my daily life?

What are the origins of this rule (or assumption)? Where did I learn it? What was going on in my life that would have made it helpful back then?

What are the advantages of this rule?

What are the disadvantages?

What are alternatives to this rule that would make it more flexible?

De-catastrophizing (Overcoming Worry)

This tool is great for talking yourself out of worrying or expecting the worst-case scenario, such as when you're making a big hairy deal about something. By looking at the facts of the situation it helps you reign in your exaggerated thinking and look more rationally at why this is happening.

What is the Catastrophe? Begins by identifying the catastrophe that you are worrying about. You should clearly state the predicted catastrophe and avoid using "What if…?" statements.

How Terrible is It? Also, rate how terrible you believe this catastrophe will be on a scale from 0% (not so bad) to 100% (absolutely awful). ____________________

How Likely is It? Once you have identified the catastrophe that is worrying you, ask yourself, "how likely the event is to actually happen?" Ask yourself whether a similar event has occurred in the past and, if so, how often it did it occur?

With the frequency of this previous catastrophe in mind, make an educated guess of how likely it is to happen. On a scale of 0% to 100%? ____________________

What is the Worst that Could Happen? What is the worst-case scenario? What is the best-case scenario? What is the most likely outcome? Try to put yourself in a friend's shoes and think about what you would say to yourself about your worry.

How Would You Cope? Once you have a good idea of how bad the catastrophe would actually be, ask yourself, "how would I cope with the fallout?" Note whether this has come to pass before and, if so, how you coped when it happened. Consider the resources you have at your disposal to help you cope, including friends and loved ones, skills or abilities you have, and methods or techniques that help you cope in other situations.

How Can You Reassure Yourself? Finally, you are directed to put together a narrative about the "catastrophe" based on the work you have done. Think about what you would like to hear in order to feel reassured, and what kind of tone would be most helpful. Once you have come up with something positive and reassuring to say to yourself about the potential catastrophe, rate how terrible you think the catastrophe will be once again.

Fear Setting

Unless your fears are very specifically defined, you cannot overcome them.

What if I ____

DEFINE (Worst Case)	PREVENT	REPAIR
Get detailed about what, exactly, you fear. Ask "so what?"	What could you do (for each) or ask someone to help you do to prevent this from happening (even if it only decreases the likelihood by 1%)?	For each, if it DID happen, what could you do to either repair the damage or get back on track?

For other workbooks and the online courses that accompany them,
visit www.transformationacademy.com.

Manufactured by Amazon.ca
Bolton, ON